To: ~~[name scribbled out]~~

I enjoyed having your future in my class in Volcanology and it was nice of you to come to see my program on Paricutin Volcano. The author of this book was a student in several of my classes —

I want to encourage you to continue your interest in Volcanos and some day I will expect to read one of your ebooks on the subject.

With best wishes

Fred M. Bullard

May 19, 1970

Juan of Parícutin

Juan
of
Parícutin

by Marion Isabelle Whitney

Steck-Vaughn Company • Austin, Texas

Preface

IN THE LIFE of every person there is an experience which stands out as his one great moment. Mine was seeing for the first time the volcano Parícutin. But despite the thrill of seeing its beauty and of sensing the great power of earth forces, I was not blind to the human tragedy which the volcanic eruption caused. Nor would my appealing little guide Juan let me forget the human side. To him, also, the volcano was the greatest event of his life. Therefore, I have woven his story and mine together in order to share our great experiences with many boys and girls.

The birth of a volcano is an unusual event and has been seen only twice in recorded history. The first time was on Teneriffe, in the Canary Islands, when the volcano Chinyera came into existence in 1909. Parícutin's birth was on February 20, 1943.

When I was small, I used to ask my mother if the stories which I read were "real." To you who will ask that question about this story, I will answer: of course it is. I saw Grandfather and Grandmother, all so gaily dressed, and I bargained with Papá. Pedro was my guide in Uruapan; Juan, at the volcano. One of my friends rode Macho and laughed at his churning ears.

Nothing was more real than the destruction and the terror that the volcano caused. I have tried to tell you what the volcano meant to Juan and his friends. Since I am a geologist, I have tried to tell you what Parícutin meant to geologists. I have looked through the windows of memory a thousand times upon Parícutin's great billowy cloud, curling high into the sky, and a thousand times have relived my first glimpse of its dark cone through the dead trees. I can still hear its roar and feel the quivering ground. As often as I see the black rivers of rock covering the little town of San Juan de Parangaricutiro, my heart sinks, for there come Mamá and Grandmother trudging barefoot in the deep ash, weeping, and struggling with the long boards from their home tucked under their arms.

It is these treasures of memory that I want to share.

—Marion Isabelle Whitney

Acknowledgments

THE AUTHOR wishes to express her appreciation to the many persons who have helped in the making of this story by their encouragement and suggestions.

Special appreciation is due the following: Dr. and Mrs. F. L. Whitney for numerous suggestions; Dr. and Mrs. Fred M. Bullard for much of the geologic information and for the use of their pictures, which were the original inspiration for the writing of the story; Dr. Cora Martin for her careful analysis of the story in the early period of its growth and for her many valuable suggestions; Mrs. Truman McEver and Mrs. Roy Bedichek for their help with the fiesta scenes and other cultural portions of the story; and Mrs. Gerald Stafford for the numerous classroom tests she made with it and for the fine suggestions which grew out of these tests.

The author also expresses appreciation to Miss Helen Wadel, whose picture appears in the frontispiece, for accompanying her to the volcano, since these trips alone made possible the creation of this book.

1.

The Fiesta

THE SUN was just peeping over the distant mountains when early one morning María called her little son.

"Juan, it's washday! Get up! We must get the work done early this morning."

"Oh, Mamá, must we wash today? This is such a wonderful day for a fiesta. I wish there were a fiesta to go to."

"But there *is,* Juan! That is why we must get our work done early — so that we can go to it."

Juan jumped up and pulled on his clothes, while María poured corn into the *metate,* the hollowed rock in which she always ground the grain.

"Here, Juan, you grind the corn for breakfast," she said, putting the *metate* into his hands.

Mamá had soaked the corn in limewater until it was soft. Then she had put it through a colander to remove the hulls of the kernels.

Juan sat down on the dirt floor of their little home and put the *metate* between his knees. With a big flattened stone he ground the corn fine.

In western Mexico, in the state of Michoacán, little boys do not run to the store to buy their mothers a box of corn meal. They grow the corn and grind it themselves.

Juan was just ten years old. He lived in the tiny village of Parícutin. Like all other little Tarascan Indian boys, he had many chores to do for both his father and his mother. His father José had big brother Manuel to help him, but he expected Juan to hoe the corn, look after the sheep, milk the cows, feed the donkeys, and run errands.

As Juan had no sister, he had to help his mother with the woman's work also. He did not like to do woman's work, but since his mother was strict with him, he did some chores which he felt were beneath his dignity. But he had time to play, too. There was no school in Parícutin to take up his time.

"Mamá, the corn is ground," said Juan, as he handed her the *metate*.

"Good! Now, Juan, I need some water. I shall use the last in the jug for breakfast."

Juan picked up the big brown pottery jug and ran to the creek to get the drinking water. He dipped his jug into the cool spring beside the creek and brought it up full of sparkling water. Carefully he balanced the jug on his head and walked back to the house, holding himself very straight. Never a drop did he spill!

Meanwhile, María was making the tortillas. She kneaded the moist, ground corn with a stone roller. Then she patted it into thin cakes. These she cooked on a large, flat clay griddle, which sat upon three piles of stones. María used charcoal to make the fire under the griddle, and she used a reed mat for a windbreak.

When breakfast was done, Papá took Manuel out to the cornfield. It was close to planting time, and the ground had to be prepared.

3

Manuel wanted to go to the fiesta, too, but Papá thought he should work awhile before he went.

"Come, Juan, let's get the clothes washed," said Mamá. "We must leave early to go to the markets. We don't want to miss the fun!"

Oh, how Juan wished for a sister on wash-days! But he did not complain. He just picked up the basket of clothes and carried it to the bank of the creek.

Mamá brought a kind of soap made from weeds. Kneeling on the creek bank, she and Juan rubbed each piece of clothing with soap and then scrubbed the clothes on the stones in the creek until all the dirt was washed away. It was hard work!

Although Juan usually wore dark clothes, Papá and Manuel wore coarse white cotton trousers, which lapped across the front and were tied around the waist. Papá and Manuel did such hard, dirty work that their trousers became very grimy, and it took so long to rub them clean on the stones that Juan wore nearly all the skin off his little hands before Mamá let him stop rubbing.

Suddenly Juan heard someone coming along the creek bank. He looked up and shouted, "Uncle Dionisio!"

"Juan, are you going to the fiesta today?" called Uncle Dionisio.

"Oh yes, we are hurrying to get our work done so we can go. Are you going?"

"Yes, I shall go, but first I must see your father. I must get some help in my fields. Where is he?"

"Oh, he and Manuel went to our cornfield to get the ground ready for planting."

"Thank you, Juan."

"I shall look for you at the fiesta, Uncle Dionisio!" called Juan, as his uncle disappeared through the bushes.

"Juan," said María, "you'd better take your bath while we are here."

Juan took off his clothes and waded into the cool creek. He splashed around a bit and then said, "I'm clean now. Let's spread the clothes out on the bank to dry. Let's hurry. We must not be late for the fiesta!"

After pulling on his clothes, he quickly began to spread out the freshly washed garments on the grassy bank.

Looking up after awhile, he saw his grandmother and his grandfather coming over the bank. He shouted for joy, "*¡Hola,* Grandfather! *¡Hola,* Grandmother!"

It had been a long time since he had seen them. They lived in the town of San Juan, three miles away, where the fiesta was being held. Of course, three miles was not really a great distance, but it was always hard for Juan's family to leave home. There was always so much to be done.

Grandfather was a stately, erect old man, with snow-white chin whiskers about five inches long. He was tall, too, for Tarascan Indians are the tallest Indians in Mexico. He was thin, and his black eyes were set deep under white eyebrows. His nose was thin and high and sharp.

On his head he wore a wide-brimmed straw hat with a tapering crown and a flat top. Over his shoulder hung a long serape, which was brightly striped in red, black, yellow, orange, green, and blue. He wore white trousers and a white blouse, and on his feet were sandals made of flat leather soles, fastened to his feet by straps. They were not much like shoes, but nobody would notice that fact because Grandfather was so gaily dressed, and he sat so straight on his little donkey.

Grandmother was barefooted, and she walked beside the donkey. She wore a white cotton blouse. Her long black skirt was made of wool, with wide box pleats. At the waist the skirt flared in a frill above the drawstring which held it up. Over her shoulders was a knitted woolen shawl. It was black with big patches of red and yellow and orange. Both Grandmother and Grandfather looked very gay and happy.

Juan ran to meet them, and Grandfather said, "My little Juan, would you like to come with us to the fiesta at San Juan today?"

"Oh, yes, Grandfather. We were planning to come when we finished our work, but I should like to go to the fiesta with you!"

"Well then, run to the house and get ready, because we are going right back."

Juan hurried as fast as he could. It was

fun to go to a fiesta with Grandfather. Then suddenly he stopped running. He had remembered that his mother would be left to finish the washing alone.

"Grandfather," he called back, "maybe I had better help Mamá finish the washing."

"No, Juan, this time your mother won't mind. Will you, María?"

"No, you may get ready to go with Grandfather. Don't keep him waiting," said Mamá.

Juan ran to the house and changed his clothes. Since it was a fiesta to which he was going, he would wear his best clothes, the ones he always wore to church. Over his shoulder he threw the little serape which Mamá had woven for him. It was both his coat and his blanket.

"Grandfather, I'm ready," he called, as he ran back to the creek.

Over the fields they journeyed to San Juan, Grandfather riding his donkey, while Grandmother and Juan walked behind. Juan's feet began to get tired. He thought how Grandmother must feel. She had walked all the way

8

to Parícutin and back to San Juan. Surely she must be tired too.

Suddenly he said, "Grandfather, why does Grandmother walk while you ride?"

"Because she doesn't have a donkey to ride," said Grandfather. "If there's only one donkey, then it's the privilege of the master of the house to ride it, Juan. That has always been the custom among our people."

When the three arrived in San Juan, people were coming to the fiesta from all directions. From afar they could see that the plaza was filled with people, who had come from the surrounding country with their wares and foods to sell in the market. Juan had a happy feeling 'way down inside him. He liked to go to the market with Grandfather, and he liked the excitement of the fiesta.

Suddenly the earth under Juan's feet began to tremble. He was terrified.

"Grandfather, what is the matter? I'm shaking! The whole earth is shaking!"

"O merciful God, forgive us our sins!"

9

wailed Grandmother from the ground, where she had fallen.

Grandfather stopped his donkey. He pulled his long white beard and watched the excited crowd rushing about in the plaza. He seemed rather amused as he sat there on his donkey.

"All this excitement over a small earthquake! Come, you two, let's go on. This one did not amount to much — just a little shaking," he said.

"But, Grandfather, suppose a bigger one comes. What shall we do?"

"What *can* we do, son? We can't stop the earth from shaking. We will go to the plaza, which is wide. Nothing can fall on us there."

Slowly Grandmother picked herself up from the ground and began to trudge toward the plaza behind the donkey.

Suddenly the ground shook again, this time violently! Juan looked at the tall towers of the old church on the east side of the plaza. He thought he saw them sway. But he was swaying so much himself he couldn't be sure.

Grandmother threw herself on her face on the ground. Juan heard her groaning. He saw her saying her rosary. Grandfather did not look amused this time. Everyone in the plaza seemed to be greatly excited, and people were running out of their houses.

Grandfather sat gravely on his little donkey and looked down the street to the plaza. Then he said, "Come on, let's go. It's stopped shaking now. Nothing fell. Nobody got hurt."

"But this one was worse than the first one, Grandfather, wasn't it?"

"Yes, son. We may get more earthquakes. Maybe they will be worse. But we'll have some fun at the fiesta anyhow."

Grandmother was so frightened she could hardly get up from the ground. She prayed as she walked. When they arrived at the plaza, she said, "Let us go at once to the church and pray. Perhaps if we pray, God will not send us another fearful earthquake."

They went to the old church, which had been standing on the plaza for over three hundred years, its lofty towers reaching toward the sky. Juan and Grandmother knelt at the door, but Grandfather walked up to a statue of a saint and knelt. Then Grandmother and

Juan walked on their knees almost the full length of the long stone floor, praying as they went. They stopped at last before the image of the Virgin of Guadalupe. They touched her skirt and prayed to her, begging that no more earthquakes be sent to them.

When they had finished their prayers, they went out on the plaza, where the venders had been gathering since dawn. By this time, everyone had calmed down. All were busy putting up little tents made of white cloth, stretched between four poles to keep the sun from the foods to be offered for sale.

Juan watched all the activity on the plaza with such interest that he forgot all about the earthquakes.

Soon Grandfather said, "Come on, let's go."

"Where are we going now, Grandfather?" asked Juan.

"We are going to my home for dinner. Then we shall take our siesta and later come back to the plaza."

Juan found it hard to go to sleep during the siesta hour because he was so anxious to get back to the plaza to see what was happening

12

there. Grandfather was asleep in the patio under a palm tree. His white chin whiskers stuck straight up. Juan tiptoed up to him and gently pulled his beard.

"Wake up, Grandfather! I'm sure it's time to go."

"Oh, impatient one! Why would you cut short the siesta to see a crowd of people on the plaza? Don't you know that the dancing has not begun yet? Don't you know that the games have not started yet? Perhaps, too, the venders are still taking their siestas."

"But, Grandfather, I'm so afraid we will miss some of the fun."

"All right, we will go now."

As they walked out upon the plaza, they saw the gay market which had been set up there for this festive occasion. This was not only a day of celebration but a market day as well.

How beautiful the plaza was! There was color everywhere Juan looked. One vender had a booth with gaily painted furniture.

13

There were cane chairs with high rounded backs and bright designs woven into them. There were little black wooden chairs with cane bottoms and with bright paintings of fruit and flowers upon the legs and backs.

One vender had a booth full of wonderful baskets. They were all sizes, from the little *cestas* as tiny as a pea up to the great *canastas* as tall as Grandfather. All of them had red and green straws woven into bright stripes and designs. There were *petates,* or mats, in this booth too. These were woven of yucca, reed, or palm leaves and served for windbreaks and for beds. (Juan slept upon a *petate* on the floor of his little home in Parícutin.)

From a pole in another booth hung dark blue *rebozos,* or head scarfs, for the women. Each scarf had a narrow white stripe along its edges. Upon still another pole hung bright pink satin blouses. Here in this booth also was a shelf of large moneybags, with threads of gay blue and red and green woven into designs upon them. Another shelf held all sizes and colors of *huaraches,* or sandals. They were so woven of strips of dyed leather that they would squeak when one walked in them. On another pole there were the beautiful red and black serapes so characteristic of Michoacán.

Next door, Juan saw a huge woolen serape upon the ground. Scattered over it were big clay water jugs and enormous decorated bowls.

Still farther on, one vender had shelves full of guitars. These were polished until they gleamed in the noonday sun. (The finest guitars in all of Mexico are made in Michoacán.) Hanging from poles were long strings of gourds of every shape and size, painted in reds, yellows, greens, and blues. There were gourd rattles, gourd musical instruments, and bowls made of gourds.

Juan and Grandfather paused to look at all this gay sight. Then suddenly they realized that it was still the siesta hour in the plaza.

There was scarcely a person stirring. Women and men lay stretched out upon the roadway asleep, and some very old men were sitting on the curb asleep, with their heads resting on their arms and knees. The donkeys were staked in a lot. They stood drowsing in the sun or switching their tails and

15

stamping their little feet. Even the boys and the dogs were asleep.

"You see, Juan, you were too impatient. We have come too early."

Just then Juan saw a man sitting up, rubbing his eyes. "Look, Grandfather. He is waking up. Let's see what he has for sale."

On the ground the man had spread a white cloth, on which he had arranged rows of green, peeled cactus fruits. Juan looked eagerly at them. He could imagine how good they would taste!

"Do you want some fruit, little boy?" asked the man.

"I don't know. Grandfather, do I want any fruit?" asked Juan wistfully.

"Yes, from the look in your eye, I think you do. Take this *cinco centavos* and buy some for yourself," said the old man, with a chuckle.

"Oh, thank you, Grandfather!"

Just then a big firecracker went off with a loud bang that made Grandfather jump. Juan danced and clapped his hands with excitement as more and more firecrackers were shot off.

16

Soon all the venders were awake, and Juan was looking hungrily at their many wares. He stopped before one tent where there were peeled slices of golden-yellow pineapple. "Oh, Grandfather, couldn't you find another *cinco-centavos* piece? I just must have a slice of pineapple."

"Yes, I think I might have another *cinco centavos.*"

Juan bought his pineapple and ate it slowly, enjoying every bite. It was his favorite fruit. How delicious it was! When he had finished, they again moved along, stopping to admire all the displays. Each vender had arranged his colorful display on white cloths, and against the white the colors seemed brighter than ever. Big carrots were stacked under one tent, and near by were baskets of shelled green peas. Under another tent were rows of white onions and strings of little red *chiles.*

The prettiest of all were the fruits. One woman had big baskets of mangoes, figs, peaches, lemons, avocados, and grapefruit arranged on leaves. Of course Juan wanted some of all

17

that he saw, but Grandfather said he could not find any more *centavos*.

When they reached the pottery displays, they saw a man just coming to the market with his load of pottery. It was stacked upon shelves in a tall frame which he carried upon his back. A leather strap across his forehead held the frame in place. Behind him came two boys driving burros. All the burros carried huge, neat bundles of straw, one on each side of their backs.

"What is in those bundles, Grandfather?"

"That is pottery, wrapped so that it will not break on the way to the market, Juan."

"I'd like to watch them unload," said Juan.

Just then the burros turned a corner and disappeared. Then Grandfather said, "Let's go look at the market instead."

They turned to the pottery booths, where all the bright, colorful dishes were displayed. Juan wandered among the shelves, talking excitedly to Grandfather about each thing he saw.

"Look, Grandfather, what a big cup!"

"That is a *jícara,* or chocolate cup. Here's

At the Market

PHOTOGRAPH BY THE AUTHOR

one made out of a gourd. See what a pretty yellow color they painted it!"

Next they turned to the big long-necked water jugs, or *ollas,* and the tall drinking mugs, or *tazas,* with crude handles on them. These were striped in red upon gray clay and they were decorated with little red birds. Then there was a huge clay colander full of holes — like the one Mamá used to make tortillas.

There were rows of cups and saucers (*tazas* and *platillos*). There were stacks of plates, or

19

platos, all decorated in gay designs. Here was one set of dishes with big plumes of blue and yellow upon it. Here was another set decorated with bright oranges. Juan spied the prettiest set of all.

"Oh, look, Grandfather. See these *platos?* Look at the soldier on his beautiful black and white *caballo.* Oh, I wish I had *un caballo* to ride. See the soldier's gun, Grandfather?"

"Yes, Juan. He is a fine soldier. The man who made these *platos* was a fine artist too. His pictures are much prettier than all the rest."

Juan turned away now and suddenly noticed the shelves with the toys. "Oh, Grandfather, come look at the *figuritas.*"

He was so excited that he was dancing. All the toys were so gay and wonderful. Some were made of clay, and some were made of straw. Still others were carved of wood.

"Oh, Grandfather, here is a wooden soldier."

"He's not so nice as the ones on the *platos.*"

"Oh, but I could play with him, and I could

20

not play with the ones on the *platos*," said Juan.

His eyes moved on to other small toys. Here was a figure of China Poblana, the Chinese princess who was captured and brought to Mexico. She wore a blouse of lace and spangles, a full green skirt, and a big *sombrero*. She was beautiful, but she was for girls.

"Look, Grandfather, there is a big green bird with a whistle in his tail, perched upon a stick."

Juan almost asked Grandfather to buy the bird for him, but Grandfather said, "That bird would be fun to have, but it is not a very useful toy."

There was a little straw man upon a straw horse that Juan thought he wanted until he saw a huge green frog with black spots on his back and a jingling bell inside.

"Don't spend all your time gazing at that silly frog. There are other toys, Juan," said Grandfather.

Juan looked thoughtfully at a *figurita* of the Virgin of Guadalupe. Then his eye fell upon the manger scene, with the Babe in the cradle and the shepherds looking down upon Him.

Grandfather was moving toward the last toy shelf in the booth. Juan knew now that he must make his decision quickly on what he wanted to buy. He hurried past rows of little carved donkeys and Indians taking their siestas. Some were made of dyed stone — rich red, pale blue, lemon yellow. Oh, how pretty they were! They would be nice to have, but he wanted to see everything before he made his selection. At last Grandfather stopped in front of shelves of clay animals, some with slits in their backs, some with open mouths to catch pennies.

"There now, these are useful toys," said Grandfather, with a twinkle in his eyes.

There was a big red-and-white cow with a happy expression on her face. There was another green frog with his mouth wide open. There was a small clay donkey with huge ears and a very round body that could hold lots of pennies. Then Juan saw a little fat, painted pig. He fell in love with it.

"Oh, Grandfather, I wish you did have an-

22

other *cinco centavos*. I do want this pig. See, he has a pink nose! And look at the roses on his sides! Look at his little curly tail! And he has a little handle on his back so I can carry him."

With a twinkle in his eye, Grandfather dug deep in his embroidered moneybag, which he kept tied to his waist. Out came another coin!

"I'm sure this is the last one," said Grandfather. "Now buy your pig."

Juan jumped for joy as the old man handed him the money. He quickly completed the purchase, and proudly he carried his pig through the market place.

People had begun to gather now, and the smell of roasting corn was in the air. "Grandfather, I smell corn. Where is it?"

"Over there, my child. See that old woman with the big black can? She has glowing charcoal in the bottom of the can. See it through the holes? She is cooking the corn over it."

Just then Juan glanced up the street and suddenly began to laugh. A woman covered with chickens was coming toward them. She certainly was a strange-looking sight. The

23

chickens were hanging upside down and flapping their wings. The woman evidently had no donkey on which to carry them. She had tied them to her waist and shoulders to bring them to market.

Juan's attention was drawn away from the woman by the sound of music.

"Listen, Grandfather, I hear something!"

"Yes, the *mariachis* have come. They will play their guitars and sing all afternoon. Then there will be dancing later, and they will play until all the dancers have dropped from fatigue. They are gay fellows. They will get drunk, and then they will roam the streets and play and sing all night. A *mariachi* just can't stop singing."

"I think I should like to be a *mariachi*. Oh, look, Grandfather! See that old man with the parrot on his shoulder? It's biting his ear! Doesn't it hurt him?"

"No, the parrot is only playing. It is very fond of the man. Watch it awhile. Parrots are very clever. They can say many words and do all sorts of tricks."

The parrot chose that very moment to say

some scolding, chattering words to its owner.

Juan laughed and said, "Grandfather, that's the kind of pet to have. How much does a parrot cost?"

"You want one for a playmate, eh?" chuckled the old man. "Well, a parrot costs more than *cinco centavos,* and I'm sure that the man loves his bird so much he wouldn't sell him. See how proudly he looks at his pet?"

The old man had seen Juan watching the bird. Now he smiled and held a stick to his shoulder. Then he told the bird to get on the stick. The parrot put out a foot and caught the stick. Then the old man lifted the little bright green-and-red bird into the air. With a squawk the parrot quickly turned upside down and began to rock back and forth, holding the stick with one foot.

"Oh, Grandfather, he is doing tricks!"

"See how proud the old man is? He wouldn't part with his pet," said Grandfather.

Juan followed the old man and the parrot around for a long time as they went from stand to stand. Sometimes the parrot would hop down from his perch on the old man's shoulder and steal some fruit. This the old man pretended not to see, unless the vender shouted at him and tried to hit the bird. Then he would scold the parrot sternly and tell it to get back on his shoulder.

After they had seen all the stands, Juan and Grandfather went to find a park bench on the plaza. Grandfather knew that it was about time for the dancing to begin, and he wanted to have a good seat. The plaza was bright with flowers in bloom everywhere. Shade trees and palms grew along the walks.

People had begun to gather in little groups around the plaza, and at one side there was forming a line of young girls wearing gay shawls. On the other side was a line of young men. Soon the *mariachis* struck up a lively tune, and the two lines of young people began to march in opposite directions. Around and around the plaza they went, girls and boys looking intently into one another's eyes, but never uttering a word.

"I don't see why they do that, Grandfather."

"You will know someday. You will be doing the same thing one of these days."

"Why do they look so at one another?"

"Well, they are picking out their sweet-hearts."

"Why don't they ever say anything?"

"They're not allowed to talk yet."

"Oh, look! There's Manuel walking with the boys! See that girl, Grandfather? See how she looks at Manuel?"

"She is a clever one," Grandfather chuckled.

"Isn't it all right to be clever, Grandfather? I think she is beautiful!"

"Oh, she is trying to steal Manuel's heart away."

"Can she do that?"

"She's done that already."

"How do you know?"

"Ah, little one! Look at Manuel. Can't you see what has happened? I can tell by the expression in his eyes."

After a while the *mariachis* stopped playing, and the lines of young people broke up. Some of the boys and girls lingered, looking at one another from a distance. Some found partners and chatted gaily. Juan saw Manuel and the beautiful girl sauntering off through the market place together, and he wondered whether she had really stolen Manuel's heart away. If she had, it must surely be all right, because Manuel seemed pleased.

Soon the dancers came, dressed in colorful costumes, and the dances started. Of all the dances, the old men's dance amused Juan the most. It was very funny. Young men danced this one with huge, ugly masks over their heads. The faces of the masks looked like toothless old men, with long noses that nearly touched their chins. They had long, thin, matted white hair and big beady eyes. It seemed strange for "old men" to jump about so fast.

The dancers were bent nearly double and leaned heavily on stout canes. But it was a wild, vigorous dance that only a young man could do. They pretended to be angry, and they would shake their big knotty canes at one another as they stumped around over the ground. They shook their big ugly masks too.

"Oh, look, Grandfather! What ugly faces!"

exclaimed Juan. "Oh, see how the men fight!"

Grandfather looked amused. The crowd was cheering. Juan laughed until his sides hurt.

Soon raindrops fell right on Juan's nose. "Of course it has to start raining right now!"

"Let's go stand in a shelter until the rain stops."

They hurried to the nearest doorway and stepped inside.

The dancers and the crowd scattered. Some of the men unrolled their raincoats, which they carried in big, thick rolls on their backs. These coats were made of shaggy palm leaves and shed water just like the thatched roofs of the houses. The men who wore them walked around in the shower, looking like big pineapples turned upside down.

"Grandfather, you know, I have a raincoat like that. I wear it on rainy days when I go to look after our sheep. Manuel made it for me. I brought only my serape today, though," said Juan.

The downpour suddenly stopped, and the clouds cleared away. Then the crowd came back, and the dancing began again. On and on they danced, until the sun set.

Through the dusk there came the sound of firecrackers again. Juan began to dance with delight.

"When do the fireworks begin, Grandfather?"

"Right now! Let's get out on the open part of the plaza and watch them."

Juan and Grandfather pushed their way through the crowd to a bench. Others were coming now to the open plaza. The excitement was great. The little boys were all tense and expectant over the events to come. Suddenly with the loud bang of a giant firecracker the display began. There were brilliant showers, fountains, skyrockets that showered little balloons of colored fire, wonderful wheels, and noisy torpedoes. Everyone shouted, *"¡Qué bonito!"* as each display lighted the sky. Soon strains of music were heard.

"Oh, the *mariachis* are calling the dancers again, Grandfather. Soon all these wonderful fireworks will be over. I wish they would go on all night," said Juan.

30

"Well, son, after awhile, they will use up all their fireworks. Then they have to stop. I think they shot their last one with that big fountain, but we will sit awhile longer and wait to see if there are any more."

As soon as it was dark, Juan began to feel sleepy, and in no time at all Grandfather felt a heavy little head against his arm. He shook Juan gently.

"Wake up, boy! Let's go home."

"Grandfather, I just can't keep my eyes open any longer."

"Get up and move fast. Then you will get them open. Don't you like the fiesta?"

"Oh, yes! It is the most wonderful fiesta I have ever seen. It is so gay and so beautiful! But I'm used to going to bed when it begins to get dark. I can't keep my eyes open."

"All right. Hurry now, and you shall go to bed soon, little sleepyhead."

Just then rumbling came from out of the earth. The ground seemed to surge in waves under Juan's feet. It seemed as though the world would fly apart. It made him feel queer inside — almost ill. He could not stand. He fell to the ground. Then he got up and looked at Grandfather, who seemed to be swaying like a tall pole.

"Oh, Grandfather, the terrible thing has come again!"

In his ears rang the screams of the frightened women, who were falling on their faces.

All the little tents were shaking violently. Suddenly a great tremor flattened them out over the displays of the venders. Fruit was rolling all over the trembling ground as it spilled from the venders' baskets. The donkeys were stamping their feet and braying. Everywhere there were cries and confusion.

"Grandfather! Even the donkeys are afraid!"

Juan was nearly crying.

"Yes, son. We all need to be afraid because the earthquakes are growing stronger. They may do some terrible thing. But what can we do to stop them but pray? Where can we go? We are safer here in the plaza than in the streets or in our house. Here we can be safe from falling walls."

Grandfather sat down on the bench beside Juan and drew him close in his arms.

"Will it last long, Grandfather?"

"I don't know, son. We shall have to wait and see."

For a moment the trembling stopped. Then Juan saw frightened mothers rushing to the open spaces of the plaza with their babies so that nothing could fall on them. He saw them huddle together on the ground or on benches. Suddenly he felt as though he were moving in all directions at once. The tops of the palm trees near by bent until they almost touched the ground, first on one side, then on the other.

Down the street he could hear boards falling. People were screaming and running. Suddenly he wanted to run too, but Grandfather put a firm hand on his shoulder and said, "Sit still, Juan. You are as safe here as anywhere else."

Juan looked out across the plaza and saw people praying on the steps of the great church. Others were running toward the church in un-

33

certain, zigzag paths. He saw the great towers above them swaying.

"Grandfather, look at those towers! Look at those people under them! They will be killed!"

Grandfather got up from the bench and shouted, "Come back from the church! Come back, all of you!"

Other men shouted. They grabbed some of the people who were running to pray on the church steps. The young girls were screaming in terror as the towers swayed. The people praying loudly on the steps did not hear the men who were calling them to safety. But those who were running to the church finally turned back.

Juan saw someone tall like Manuel dash through the dusk to the church steps to warn those there and those inside that the towers were swaying dangerously.

"He's brave, Grandfather. But he may get hurt. Oh! It looks like Manuel!"

"Yes, son. It *is* Manuel! Oh, it's calming down now. Thank heaven!"

He sank down again on the bench. He seemed exhausted.

"Oh, Grandfather, I hope nothing happens to the church."

The people came running across the plaza from the church steps.

"Grandfather, look! One of those women on the steps was Grandmother. See, she can't move very fast. Oh, look! One was Mamá, too."

Juan broke away from Grandfather's grip and grabbed his mother.

"Oh, Mamá, Mamá! Are you all right? Look, Grandfather is over on that bench!"

Then he dashed out to meet Grandmother.

"Oh, Grandmother, I'm so glad you are not hurt. Any minute now the towers may fall!"

Grandmother walked as fast as she could to the bench. The little family crowded together and waited to see what would happen.

The earth continued to tremble at intervals, and the people moaned and screamed and prayed. Little groups were huddled here and there on the broad plaza. A few persons dashed down the middle of the streets to avoid the falling debris from the houses. On out into the country they rushed to safety.

"Grandfather, why don't we go to the country too?"

"Because I can't move fast enough if the buildings start to fall. Look at those cracks in the wall of this nearest house. See all those boards and the rubbish in the street? If more should fall, I could not get out of the way. We will stay here. Nothing can fall on us here, not even the great stone church towers."

"There are so many people in the plaza. If the towers fall, surely someone will be hurt, for they cannot all get as far away as we are, Grandfather."

"Perhaps so, son. We can only wait and hope that no one is hurt. It's calmer now. Maybe nothing more will happen. It will stop sometime."

But Grandmother wailed, "Surely this is the end of the world!"

Papá came out of the darkness, and Mamá grabbed his arm.

"Oh, José, I'm so glad to see you! I am afraid."

36

"Be calm, María. Nothing serious has happened yet — only a few boards in the streets, a few cracks in the houses. Maybe it will be all right."

"Where is Manuel, José?" asked Mamá.

"Oh, you may be sure he is safe somewhere."

"Papá, I think I see Manuel over by the bandstand. He has his arm around that girl, and she is crying," said Juan.

"All the women are crying," said José. "Look at your mother and your grandmother. All this crying. What good does it do to cry? Crying will change nothing."

Just then a severe trembling of the earth shook Juan off the bench. Papá was sitting on the ground, and Juan rolled right into his lap.

Piercing shrieks went up from the plaza. In the dim light of dusk Juan could see the great towers swaying. Suddenly there was a cracking sound from above that was louder than the din on the ground.

Juan scrambled to his feet.

"Oh, the tower!" he screamed.

He saw the great blocks of limestone pull apart as the tower swayed. Then, with a thun-

37

derous crash, the south tower fell apart and came tumbling into the plaza.

There were frantic screams and a wild scrambling, but Juan's family stood as though rooted to the ground.

Grandfather listened closely to all the clamor. Then he said, with a pleased expression, "Nobody got hurt!"

"But how can you tell?" asked Juan. It seemed to him that the people must surely be in pain.

"Those are only screams of fear, not pain," said Grandfather.

Papá was running out across the plaza now, and so was Manuel. Juan wanted to go too, but Grandfather's hand was heavy on his shoulder, and he could not move.

Soon Papá came back. "Grandfather was right!" he shouted, as he came near. "Nobody was hurt. Blocks of rock fell all around people and rolled away out on the plaza, but none fell on anyone."

"Oh, a miracle by the Holy Mother!" cried Grandmother.

People were rushing frantically past Juan

and his family toward the streets that led to the country.

"Papá, shouldn't we go too?" asked Juan.

"No, son, we are a long way from the other tower. It could not fall on us. Be calm."

Juan did not feel calm. The palms were swaying near by and people were screaming and running. Any minute the other tower could fall. He wanted to cry. But Papá had said that the women were doing the crying. Juan held back the tears and huddled close to Mamá.

Soon he realized that the earth had stopped shaking. He sat very still. Nobody was saying a word. But he knew that the family was hoping the same thing — that this was the last of the terror. It was hard to believe that this could be true.

All over the plaza, silence fell. It was as if the people were holding their breaths in fear, in disbelief, in hope.

It was dark now. The stars were out, and the moon was coming up. Juan could see the great white blocks of limestone scattered near the church steps. He shuddered as he remem-

39

bered that Mamá and Grandmother had been there under the swaying towers only a short while before the south tower toppled. The church was going to look queer now with just one tower. He was thinking that for three hundred years the old church had had two majestic towers. All his life he had heard the bells in these towers ringing out across the fields. Now in the space of seconds one tower was gone. He would never hear its bell again. How terrible is the earthquake! Did God send it, as Grandmother said, to punish one's sins? What were the sins? Oh, how sleepy he felt! A heavy little head fell over on Mamá.

The moon climbed higher. The plaza remained quiet. The earth was still. But the Indians waited on in silence. An hour passed — perhaps more. Then from the distance the strains of guitar music came to them. The *mariachis* were coming back. Their song rose on the night air. There was a stir in the plaza. It was as if the people came to life, stirring to the lilt of the music.

Grandfather said, "I think it will be safe

to go home now. Wake the sleepyhead, María."

Mamá shook Juan and pushed him to his feet.

"We are going to Grandfather's house now. Wake up, Juan."

"I can't wake up, Mamá," said Juan, as he stumbled over a sleeping man in the street. He was so sleepy — and so tired. Only Mamá's hold on his arm kept him from falling. He stumbled on a few steps over boards and parts of houses which had fallen in the street. Then he heard the *mariachis*.

"Oh, the *mariachis!*" he exclaimed. He was waking up now. "Grandfather, is the earthquake over?"

"Yes, Juan, I think so. Anyway, we are going home. The others can sleep in the plaza if they like. I'm going to sleep in my bed!"

"What a terrible way to end a fiesta!" said Juan, as he entered Grandfather's house.

Grandfather put him to bed, and soon Juan was dreaming of the wild dancers, the green parrot, and the beautiful dark-eyed girl who

41

had stolen Manuel's heart. He didn't dream of the earthquake a single time.

Before the sun was up the next morning, Juan was pulling at Grandfather's beard.

"Wake up, Grandfather! Let's go see what that terrible earthquake did to the beautiful church!"

"Oh, Juan, you are always in such a hurry! All right, now that I am awake, we will go; but first we must eat our tortillas."

"Oh, Grandfather, must we wait for breakfast?"

"Why not? The tower fell. The stones won't run away, impatient one!"

To Juan it seemed that Grandfather ate his breakfast slower than ever. He wished that he had run down the street to the plaza by himself. Grandfather never did walk fast.

Finally Grandfather said, "Impatient one, I've finished now. Let's go!"

They walked down the narrow street which led to the plaza. Debris from the shaken houses lay everywhere. Juan vaguely remembered his sleepy march through all the rubbish the night before.

Out on the plaza he saw the Indians stirring, collecting their wares that had been scattered by the earthquake and packing them on their donkeys. The ground was covered with fruit, and the little boys were making a game of trying to see who could pick up the greatest amount of it. The venders were also gathering up what they could save. The plaza was covered with wreckage and litter. The neat white tents which had stood there so trimly yesterday were either sagging over the wares or lying on the ground.

"*¡Hola,* Juan!" called a voice from behind.

Juan turned and saw Uncle Dionisio.

"Oh, Uncle Dionisio, did you see what the earthquake did to the church tower?"

"Yes, Juan. One of the big stones from it fell near me. A fearful thing!"

The little boys and the men were gathering now in groups around the big stones which had scattered over the east side of the plaza.

"Grandfather, let's go see the stones."

"All right, son."

43

Juan worked his way between the fallen tents, with Grandfather following behind. He picked up a beautiful yellow mango which had rolled out of someone's basket and ate it. On they went to a big heap of stones. Here the men and boys had gathered. Juan heard them planning ways to move the stones.

"See how large those stones are, Grandfather? How could anything have moved them? How can they ever be moved from the plaza?"

"Perhaps they will use the donkeys to drag them off," answered Grandfather.

He looked at the church. "It was there a long time—that tower—three hundred years!"

Juan thought he saw tears in the old man's eyes.

At home in Parícutin, Juan and Papá found a few cracks in their house.

"It's nothing," said Papá.

"A little of the thatch was shaken loose from the roof," said Juan. "But Manuel can easily fix that."

"We were more fortunate than those in San Juan," said Papá.

Even as he spoke, the earth began to move under their feet.

"Oh, Papá, here it is again!"

Mamá fell to her knees to pray.

As suddenly as it had come, the movement stopped.

Again and again in the weeks that followed, little earthquakes came to shake the people into fear. But they ceased quickly, causing scarcely any damage. Gradually they came to cause only a small bit of excitement and were accepted as a regular part of daily life.

2.

A Volcano Is Born

ONE DAY early in February, Juan's Uncle Dionisio came to see Papá again to ask for help in getting the ground ready for spring planting.

Papá agreed to go up to the field with him and to take the family along to help. Juan was delighted to have the chance to go. He began bustling about, gathering a few things he wished to take with him. Suddenly he had the bad dizzy feeling which he had felt so many times before.

"It's another earthquake!" he shouted.

The ground was quivering violently under his feet. Some of Mamá's pottery cups fell to the ground and broke. Juan looked at the shelf where he had put the little clay pig which Grandfather had bought for him. The pig was rocking back and forth. He ran to it, and it fell into his hands.

He turned to Papá with big frightened eyes. "Oh, Papá, this is the worst one yet!"

"Yes, it is. God must be very angry with us to send so many earthquakes," said Papá.

"What have we done to anger Him?" asked Juan.

"I don't know, Juan. There — the shaking has stopped. Let us pray now. Maybe God will forgive us and not send another one."

Juan dropped to his knees beside his father and his uncle. Squeezing his clay pig tightly, he prayed. But another and much stronger quake came and shook the little square frame-and-plaster house so hard that cracks opened in the walls, and Juan could see the light through them. He was more frightened than he had ever been before. The house might fall apart!

"It might be safer if we go outdoors," said Papá.

They went into the street. All the neighbors were there, on their knees, praying. Everyone was frightened, for this earthquake seemed

47

more violent than any of those that had come since the time the tower fell.

All day the quakes came. And on through the night they rocked the little community. It seemed as though they would never stop. Day after day they came, increasing in number, in strength, and in force. In one day alone there were three hundred of them. Papá counted them! Still they continued, sometimes with strange rumbling sounds coming from the hills.

It was two weeks before Juan's family could finally go to help Uncle Dionisio. As the little band of Indians approached the field, it seemed to them that the earth shook constantly and that the quakes were more intense than they had been in the village.

The cornfield was in a sort of basin about a mile and a half from the town of Parícutin. A ridge separated it from the town, and on the other side were high mountains. A deep canyon lay between the field and the mountains.

With sticks the Indians began loosening the

earth, so that the corn might be planted easily. The planting could be delayed no longer. They must have corn or they would starve. Then suddenly a deep rumbling came out of the ground close by. José dropped to his knees and laid his ear close to the earth. The others gathered about, talking excitedly.

"What is it, José?" asked María.

"Hush! It is the voice of the Devil!"

The rumbling grew louder, and the earth shook with fury. Juan was so frightened at the noise that he could scarcely tell whether it was he or the earth that was shaking. He looked from face to face. The terror he felt was expressed in the eyes of all about him. The noise seemed to be coming from only a short distance away. Everyone feared to look upon the face of the Devil. They felt that everything connected with the earthquakes was caused by him. They cringed near the earth and prayed, not daring to look around.

Finally, curiosity overcame fear. Uncle Dionisio looked up and saw a pit opening in the cornfield right before his very eyes! The field seemed to be sinking into the earth. From the rim of the pit spread cracks from which curled upward long, thin streamers of white vapor, or smoke.

"Look!" he shouted to the others, pointing across the field. He was breathing in gasps. His eyes were wide with fright.

The center of the pit was dropping in. Around the sides rose a ring of white vapor. From the center rose a column of black dust. Everyone stood up in amazement. The pit was yawning before them. Their eyes bulged, and their mouths fell open. Fear rooted them to the ground and froze their voices.

At last, after what seemed eternity, Papá gasped in a strange, hushed voice cramped with fear, "María, it is hell opening up! It is going to swallow us!"

"O Holy Mother, save us!" sobbed María, as she dropped to her knees again.

"Papá! Papá! The Devil is throwing stones!" shouted Juan.

Just then the deep rumble changed to a deafening roar, and a great shower of stones shot skyward and then fell back around the rim of the pit.

Faster, faster came the stones, and higher and higher they shot into the sky. The Indians stood by, trembling in terror, watching the pit widen.

The hail of stones grew ever greater. Soon, blocks a foot wide began to shoot out of the gaping hole.

When the stones began to fall about the little group of Indians, they turned and ran all the way back to Parícutin to tell their neighbors what they had seen. But it was not news there. Everyone in town had already heard the roaring and had seen the stones rocketing skyward. All were in a condition of panic.

"Hell opened right before our eyes!" shouted José to his fear-stricken neighbors. "I swear before the Holy Virgin that I saw the Devil wrapped in flames rising in that cloud of smoke! He showered us with stones, and we ran!"

Word spread fast over the countryside that José had seen the Devil. Rapidly the Indians nailed together huge wooden crosses, which

51

the priest blessed. They then stood them up about their tiny village to ward off the Devil, for they held to the simple faith that the Evil One dare not come near a holy cross. To the church went all the frightened Indians to pray for protection.

After awhile Juan whispered to Papá, "Couldn't I run to San Juan to tell Grandfather about this terrible thing?"

"Oh, no, Juan! You must stay with me. Surely Grandfather has heard its roaring already. How could he keep from hearing such a terrible noise?"

"But, Papá, he will want to know that we are safe!"

"To be sure he will, Juan, but you must stay with me now. Grandfather will know in time."

All day the frightened Indians knelt before the crosses and prayed. Some were so terrified that they fell upon their faces on the ground. Never had they felt so helpless or prayed harder.

As night closed in upon the little village, the fear of the people deepened. The Indians huddled close by their crosses, weeping, praying, and groveling in the dust. No one wanted to go away from the crowd. It seemed safer to be together.

From Dionisio Pulido's cornfield came an incessant roar — an unearthly sound! Above the field played a constant fountain of brilliant red stones. Like skyrockets they streaked across the dark night sky. Up and up they shot, curved, and then fell back to earth. Thousands upon thousands of them rocketed out of the pit every hour.

Above the cornfield hung a red glow. The column of dust grew higher and higher. In the darkness, the brilliant hot stones lighted it and made it a deep red color — a fearful sight!

Juan crawled close to Papá and sat with his eyes fixed upon this monster that was wrecking his uncle's cornfield. José was on his knees, mumbling prayers in a low voice. The women were groaning and weeping. Suddenly one shrieked and fell upon her face.

Juan jumped to his feet.

"Papá, Papá, look at that enormous stone! Look, it's coming right toward us!"

The Volcano at Night

José sprang to his feet, snatching María up from the ground. The huge stone fell well beyond the ridge. José, Juan, and María slumped back to the ground, sighing with relief.

On through the night the frightful fireworks painted the sky. The stones shot ever higher and higher. From exhaustion Juan finally fell asleep upon the ground beside his father. But the older Indians kept their vigil and prayed. They asked forgiveness for the unknown sin

54

which had brought this fear and suffering upon them. They called upon the Holy Mother to intercede with God for them.

As the first rays of dawn crept up the heavens behind this monstrous thing, the Indians were astonished to see a strange new hill outlined against the sky. Uncle Dionisio thought of his cornfield and of the hunger that faced his family. He sobbed violently. Never had he felt so helpless, so discouraged, so unhappy. What could he do against this evil thing? But the healing thought came that God would take care of them. As daylight broke over the frightened group, they offered prayers of thanksgiving that they had been spared through this most terrible night of their lives.

Dionisio wanted to see his entire cornfield. He and a group of the most venturesome ones crept cautiously up the ridge and looked down into the basin. The ruined field lay spread before them.

"Oh, what a terrible sight!" exclaimed Juan as they reached the top of the ridge. Around the pit had grown a huge pile of black rough rock at least one hundred and twenty feet high. Rock was scattered all over the cornfield. The field was ruined. They could never move all those great stones.

For a long time Juan watched the huge blocks of rock flying out of the pit and falling back to build the pile higher and higher. Then the rocks began to come out faster and to fall nearer.

The roar became so great that Juan felt tired and sick from it. The fumes from this monstrous thing made him feel queer. He had never smelled anything like them before. His head felt dizzy, and he was nauseated. His eyes were full of the dust that filled the air and clouded everything.

Papá said that they had better go home. The fumes and the dust were making him ill also. And the rocks were falling too close for safety now.

Uncle Dionisio was on his knees praying to God to take this thing out of his cornfield. Poor Uncle Dionisio! Juan called to him,

"Come on, let's get away from this awful thing."

When Papá, Manuel, and Juan got home, they found a thick covering of black ash over everything. All the plants, all the roofs, the ground, and even the sheep and the donkeys were covered with it. It was on the *petates* and in the food. It was gritty. Juan's teeth crunched it as he ate his tortillas and beans that day. After that, Mamá had to keep all food carefully covered, but even so everything seemed gritty.

Juan's hair was full of the dust. It was in his eyes. It flew into his mouth when he talked. He hated this monster which was growing in Uncle Dionisio's field and making them all so uncomfortable.

He began to wonder whether the monster would go away — whether it might disappear as suddenly as it had come. Then he remembered that Papá had said that it was hell opening up, and that it would swallow them all. He trembled at the idea. He seemed to tremble so much lately.

Suddenly he thought of something. He had

to find Papá quickly. "Papá! Papá!" he called, as he ran out of the house. "Where are you?"

"I'm tying up the donkeys, Juan. What do you want? Why are you so excited?"

"Oh, Papá, don't tie up the donkeys! Let's get on them and ride away from this terrible thing up in Uncle Dionisio's field! I'm afraid to stay here. Please, Papá, may we not go away from here?"

"But we cannot do that, son. This is our home, and we must stay here. Besides, where would we go?"

"Oh, any place, Papá, just so we get away from that thing!"

"No, Juan, we cannot go. We have to stay here."

"And live with *el monstruo* roaring and showering us with rock and dust and fumes the rest of our lives?"

"Son, very soon there's going to be a meeting of all the village in the church, and we are all going to pray together. Maybe God will take the thing away if we keep on praying."

"Papá, is *el monstruo* really hell opening up, as you said?"

"Yes, Juan, I think so. What else can we think? All of us believe that. But a man came this morning from Mexico City to see it, and he calls it a 'volcano.' He says there is a much bigger one near Mexico City, but that it gives off only a little smoke now and then."

"Who is the man, Papá?"

"I don't know. But he says that he studies the earth and the rocks. That is why he has much interest in what has happened here. He wants to watch the evil thing."

"Does he know how to get rid of *el volcán,* Papá?"

"No, son. No one can do anything about *el volcán.*"

The volcano grew and grew. Within twelve days it was four hundred and fifty feet high, a huge pile of black rock, spouting and roaring! Before it was two months old, it had grown to be one thousand feet high! The field was no longer a basin. It had turned into a rapidly growing mountain, which was showering the whole countryside with rock and dust.

The young leaves came out on the trees, then withered and died. The fumes were too heavy and the ash too thick. The leaves could not live. The trees which had stayed green all winter lost their leaves, and the limbs and branches became dry and dead. The corn, which had begun to come up in other fields, was soon covered with ash and died. Old cornstalks of the previous year stuck up through the black blanket. The whole countryside for more than twenty miles around was ash-covered, and everywhere there hung a haze. As fast as the Indians prepared their ground, the black ash fell and covered the corn. People who lived a long distance from the volcano began to be frightened. Would *el monstruo* send the ash over their land also? It seemed to be creeping toward them.

One day when Papá came home from a journey to Uruapan, he said to María, "We are not the only ones suffering from the ash."

"How far away has it fallen?" asked María.

"It is six inches thick everywhere, for more than twenty miles in every direction. The grass in the pastures is covered. There is no food for the cattle and the sheep in all this part of the country. Even the goats can find nothing to eat. The leaves of the trees and bushes were so covered with ash that the sun could not get to them. They withered and fell off."

"José, what shall we do? How can we eat if nobody in all this country can grow food?"

"María, the sheep are dead in the fields of some farmers. I have bought feed for mine. I cannot do that long. Some farmers have sent their stock very far away to pastures. Others have sold theirs. Soon we must decide what to do. It is nearly summer, María, but there is not a green leaf anywhere for our stock to eat! Everywhere it looks like winter. Every day, every hour, the ash grows thicker and thicker."

"José, if you sell the stock, you still must keep the donkeys and the horses to bring us food and to take us away if this monstrous volcano should cover our village."

Papá did not say anything. He choked on the dust and looked far away across the great black blanket of ash. Juan wondered if Papá would ever move away. A few of their neighbors had gone, but most of them were clinging as stubbornly to their homes as Papá was to his. Papá had been going as far away as Uruapan to buy food and hay. This was a long journey through the woods — twenty miles or more. The donkeys were slow. Sometimes Papá was gone for days. Almost all the food in the house would be gone by the time he returned. Papá was not rich. If he had nothing to sell, how could he go on buying food? Juan was worried.

3.

Juan Visits Pedro

ONE DAY Papá said to Juan, "Now it is decided. We must sell our sheep. Manuel and I are going to drive them to Uruapan. You have never been there. Would you like to go with us?"

"Oh, yes, Papá. I should love to go to Uruapan. I have never been anywhere except to San Juan."

"All right, then, you must be up early tomorrow morning."

Juan could hardly sleep. He was so anxious for morning to come! At the first rays of light, he sprang out of bed and ran to feed the donkeys. He had their wooden saddles on their backs when Papá and Manuel awakened.

Soon they were on their way, driving their

little flock of sheep to market. The sheep did not move very fast. The sun began to get hot, and Juan became tired.

"How far is it to Uruapan, Papá?"

"It is about twenty miles."

"How long shall we stay?"

"We shall be gone about three or four days and shall stay with my brother López. You can play with your cousin Pedro."

Juan had never seen Pedro, but the thought of having someone to play with made him forget all about being tired.

It was nearly dark when they arrived in Uruapan. They had to go down a long hill and past rows of big trees as they entered the town. The streets were paved with small rough cobblestones. Juan had never seen a paved street before. He said to Papá, "Uruapan is so beautiful."

"Yes, Juan, the people here say it is like heaven."

All the houses they passed were covered with white plaster and were joined together. Their roofs were made of red tile. Some houses had two stories. Juan had never seen a house

64

with two stories. The houses were close to the street. They had beautiful windows decorated with frescoes around the edges. There was always a little iron grillwork balcony at each window also.

Children and dogs played on the sidewalks and in the streets. Little naked babies toddled around the doorways. Stately women wearing dark blue scarfs over their shoulders were carrying brown jugs of water balanced on top of their heads. They were coming from a beautiful park where there were springs at which the jugs had been filled.

Everything was peaceful and restful.

Suddenly Juan heard a terrible noise behind him. Turning, he saw something that was big and black coming very fast down the street right toward him. He was so frightened that he made his little donkey walk onto the sidewalk. He even tried to drive it through one of the doorways, but a woman inside would not let him come in.

"Go away!" she shouted.

Then he heard other sounds above the shouting, and he realized that Papá and Manuel were laughing. They laughed so hard that they nearly fell off their donkeys. The big black thing passed very fast, but Juan was still trembling when Papá said, "Juan, why did you run away?"

"Oh, Papá, I thought that thing was after me and was going to kill me. What was it?"

"That was an automobile, Juan."

"What's an automobile?"

"You have never seen one before, have you?"

"No."

"Of course not, because we do not have any roads outside of our little town for an automobile to run on. Juan, people ride in it, and they don't have to kick its sides the way you do your donkey to make it go."

"What makes it go?"

"They burn something inside of it, and this causes the automobile to move."

Juan was puzzled because he could not understand how burning something inside it would make the automobile go. Just as he was about to ask another question, Papá said, "Here we are. This is López's house."

He got down from his donkey and went inside. Soon he returned with Uncle López and Pedro and introduced them to Juan. Then he told them how frightened Juan had been when he saw the automobile, and all of them laughed — even Juan.

"Pedro will have to take Juan to the station to see the train. He will really be frightened then!" said Uncle López.

"What's a train?" asked Juan.

"Oh, you will have to see one. I can't tell you," said Pedro. "Come on, let's go to the station. A train will be coming in soon."

Pedro climbed upon the donkey with Juan, and they rode toward the station. On the way, they passed a beautiful plaza and an old church. Sometimes when they passed a doorway, they could look through it to see a lovely patio with flowers and fruit trees inside.

On and on they went. Uruapan seemed to Juan to be the biggest city in all the world. It was dark now, and lights suddenly came on. Juan saw that there were lights on tall posts along the streets. They were not ordinary lanterns. All of them lighted up at once, and no one was near them. It almost frightened him. He asked Pedro about them.

"Oh, those are electric lights. We have them in our house. The light company sends us power over a wire."

Juan was so puzzled that he could not ask a question. Soon he saw a building that was lighted up as bright as day.

"This is the station. Any minute now the train will come in. I think I hear it whistling," said Pedro.

Soon there was a terrible clang and rattle. The ground shook. Juan was used to the shaking of ground, but the rattle and clang were new. It seemed as though his ears could not stand the noise. He wanted to run away, but he was afraid Pedro, too, would laugh at him, in the way Papá and Manuel had laughed. He sat still on the donkey as the huge black locomotive with its blinding light rushed past him, puffing big clouds of smoke.

When he saw the flames shooting out of the firebox, he said, "Trains must run, too,

68

by burning something inside, like the auto-mobile. Pedro, what is a train for?"

"People ride on trains from one town to another. Juan, you are a funny boy. You have never seen an automobile or an electric light or a train. Where have you been all your life?"

"In Parícutin. We don't have such things there. But we have something you don't have. I'll bet you've never seen a *volcán!* That's what we have. It used to be very quiet in Parícutin before *el volcán* grew up in Uncle Dionisio's cornfield."

"Oh, Juan, we heard it roar, and we felt the earthquakes. Our air has been full of the dust. We have ash from it all over every-thing."

"Pedro, the ash you have here is nothing. At Parícutin, we are buried in it. Papá has to shovel a path to our door every few days so we can get into our house. You should come to see the terrible volcano and the great black blanket upon the fields!"

"I should like to come," said Pedro.

"It will make you sad. It has ruined our

land. There is nothing left for the stock, or even for us, to eat. Papá had to sell his sheep because they were hungry."

"Juan, what did the earthquakes do to your town?"

"Oh, they cracked some of our houses and tore the thatch off the roofs. That was nothing compared to what they did to the beautiful old church in San Juan. I was at the market and the fiesta in San Juan when the earthquake shook one of the stone towers of the church to the ground."

"Did you see it fall?" asked Pedro.

"Of course, Pedro. I was on the plaza when the tower fell. It swayed back and forth. People screamed and crowded together. The tower cracked, and then it crashed to the ground."

"Did anybody get hurt?"

"No, Pedro, but you should have heard them scream!"

"We had lots of earthquakes here," said Pedro. "Mamá got very excited. A few boards fell. But it really wasn't so exciting as Mamá

70

thought. Of course, I was a bit scared, though, when they were very bad."

"Pedro, you should have seen *el volcán* being born. You should have seen how he threw stones!"

As the boys rode slowly back home, Juan told the story of the volcano.

On the way, Juan saw young men on the sidewalks under the pretty windows. Girls were standing on the balconies, and sometimes the men held the girls' hands. Sometimes they sang songs to them and played on guitars. Pedro told him that the men were making love to the young ladies. Juan thought of the girl who had looked at Manuel at the fiesta. He was still wondering if she had stolen Manuel's heart. Manuel would never tell when Juan asked him. Juan wanted to watch the young men making love, but Pedro reminded him that supper was probably ready by now.

Oh, how peaceful it seemed here! How happy everyone was! It reminded him of the days that would never come back to his tiny, ruined village, where now all the people were frightened over the hunger which faced them.

The next day Pedro took Juan to see the shops. There were beautiful serapes, baskets, pottery, and fruits in the shops around the plaza. But what interested Juan most were the lacquer shops. Here men and women were making boxes and trays and painting beautiful designs on them. They rubbed the lacquer until it gleamed. Juan stood in silence as he watched the men put hinges on the boxes and make the designs.

At last Pedro proudly said, "Uruapan has the most famous lacquer work in Mexico."

Juan wanted to watch the lacquer workers all day, but Pedro said, "Oh, let's go see the park. It is far more interesting. We can play there."

When they arrived at the park, he said, "This is a government park. It is one of the prettiest in all of Mexico."

There were beds of red roses and blue and

72

yellow pansies. Under the trees grew the bright red Aztec lilies.

Juan ran to a basket hanging from a limb. "Pedro, Pedro!" he called. "Come look at this lovely flower."

"Juan, we grow that in our own yard. It is an orchid. It is truly a magnificent flower. In Mexico City you would pay thirty *pesos* for one like this."

"Thirty *pesos* for a flower! Pedro, don't flowers grow free for everybody?"

"Not all of them, Juan. Some people make their living by selling flowers. Some orchids must have special care. See, this one is growing in moss. People don't plant them in dirt. Look at those growing on the trunk of the avocado tree. They get all that they need for growth from the air and from the little dirt and moisture on the bark."

Juan reached out to touch the delicate lavender flower in the basket.

"Oh, Juan, you must not touch it! You will ruin it. Since this park belongs to the government, we do not pick flowers here. When we get home, you may pick the orchids in our

73

garden. Don't you have flowers in Parícutin?"

"Pedro, we used to. Everyone had flowers. But now there is not one green leaf anywhere — not one flower!"

Suddenly a harsh squawk came from overhead. The boys looked up and saw sitting on a limb a huge red macaw with a long tail.

"Pedro, look at that parrot! It is the biggest I've ever seen."

"He's a pet of the caretaker's. Say, Juan, can you guess what those bunches of big fruits 'way up in the top of the trees are?"

"They look like grapefruit, Pedro, but I never saw such tall grapefruit trees. They are twice as high as this big house!"

"That's what they are, though — grapefruit trees. Do you know what these small trees with green berries are?"

"No, I've never seen them before."

"Well, they are coffee trees. They have to grow in the shade. That's why you will find them only under giant trees like these. When the coffee beans are ripe, they will be bright red."

74

"Pedro! What a big banana tree! I've never seen one like it!"

"Yes, the banana trees grow to be forty feet tall, and the trunks are three feet thick. Just look at those huge leaves, Juan! They grow all the way up from the ground to the tops of the trees. The trunk is made of all the leaves wrapped one around another. That biggest tree has a blossom on it, Juan. Isn't it queer looking?"

The long banana stalk curved outward and downward from the top of the tree. Little bright green bananas grew upward all along the stalk. At the end was a big cone-shaped mass of purple leaves. This was the flower.

"Come on! Let me show you something really pretty," said Pedro.

Down the shady gravel path the boys walked. Here and there the sun winked through the tall trees and splattered golden light on the moss-covered walls which lined the path. At last they came to a quaint little rustic bridge made of cedar logs. Pedro ran out on it and

75

called, "Look, Juan! Come see the little creek!"

There beneath the lovely little bridge was a stream of sparkling water.

"That's beautiful, Pedro. Look at those bright green plants waving under the water. Are there fish in the water?"

"No, this is spring water, which has been piped across the big creek just to make the park more beautiful. There are fish in the other creek, but we have to go outside of the park to do our fishing. Let's go see the water-falls."

On down the path they went. At last they came to the gorge of the big creek.

"Right here the gorge is only about twenty feet deep, but up by the springs it is about seventy-five feet deep and has steep walls. We will go up to that part later. I want to go wad-ing first," said Pedro.

"Oh, that will be fun!" exclaimed Juan.

Ahead of them was a beautiful little foam-ing waterfall. Below the falls the water rushed swiftly between big rounded rocks, murmur-ing and gurgling as it rushed along. Where

76

the stream bed widened, the creek slowed. Here the water leisurely flowed through a knee-deep pool.

"Come, let's go down to the creek and play, Juan," said Pedro, who was already running down the bank along a winding path that was bordered by tall bamboo canes and huge elephant-ear plants.

"Let's roll up our pants," said Pedro, when they reached the stream. "Roll them high, Juan. That water is deeper than it looks. Now, let me take your hand, because these round rocks are slippery."

Out across a sandy bar Pedro led Juan. Suddenly Juan sank into the sand almost up to his knees.

"Pedro! Pedro!" he screamed. "I can't pull my feet out!"

Juan seemed to be disappearing. He was terrified. Struggling, he looked at Pedro. Pedro also was buried up to his knees, but he did not seem afraid. In fact, he was giggling.

"Pedro, I'm going down! I can't get out! I'm going to be buried. It's not funny, Pedro! Help! Help!"

Pedro just laughed and let Juan struggle for a moment. Then he said, "Put your hand on that rock beside you and pull one foot at a time."

With a great sucking sound, Juan freed one foot and placed it on the rounded boulder; then he pulled the other foot out. What a relief!

"Pedro, you did that on purpose!" he shouted.

"Sure I did. I wanted to show you the quicksand. It really is the ash from your volcano. It is six inches deep on the bank, but here in the creek it is much deeper in some places. If you get out far enough, where it is really deep, you might sink out of sight. As long as you stay close to the rocks, you can pull yourself out. But you must not let the sand get above your knees. I like to play in the shallow part. It has a solid bottom. Let's go wading in the part of the creek where there is no ash."

Into the shallow creek he ran, splashing water all over Juan. On up the stream he led Juan, through the swift current, to look at the waterfall. The spray hit them in the face. The water swirled and foamed in the plunge-basin below the falls. How wonderful this beautiful creek was!

"Let's go up to the deep gorge and see the covered bridge," said Pedro.

They climbed back to the path which led to a quaint bridge made of cedar and covered with thatch. The bridge stood high above the creek. Juan felt dizzy as he looked down at the water rushing along, far below him.

Across the creek and up a way, the canyon walls rose above them, steep and sheer. Over them fell long, filmy, white waterfalls. They looked like lace curtains hung upon the rock walls. The springs, issuing from between limestone ledges, dropped away in these lovely sheet-like falls to the creek far below. From the bridge, little paths ran to fern-covered ledges where women were dipping water out of small springs into their jugs.

"Oh, how beautiful!" exclaimed Juan.

"We think this park is so beautiful it must be like heaven!" said Pedro.

Near the bridge a huge black pipe ran

across the creek high above the water. Juan gazed at it.

"That is the pipe which brings water to the pretty little creek which we saw first. It also carries water into town and to our homes. Most of the houses in Uruapan have running water in them," said Pedro.

It seemed very queer to Juan for a house to have running water in it. Pedro spoke again.

"Juan, let me show you something that I can do."

He ran to the end of the bridge and walked out upon the big black pipe.

Juan held his breath. The creek rushed along thirty feet below Pedro, but he walked fearlessly to the middle of the pipe and then turned back. From the bridge Juan watched and cheered, but he was very much afraid that Pedro might slip.

When Pedro returned, Juan said, "Pedro, you're very brave, but I was afraid that you were going to fall."

"I wasn't," said Pedro. "I've walked that

80

pipe a thousand times. We'd better go back to town now."

"But I want to learn to walk the pipe, Pedro," said Juan.

"Not now, Juan; it's nearly suppertime. Mamá will be angry if we don't return soon."

As they walked along the lovely paths under the tall avocado trees, Juan thought that he knew why people of Uruapan said their town was like heaven. He had never seen so many new and wonderful things.

On the streets once more, Juan saw a man with a small gray fox on a chain. The man called Juan over and asked him if he wanted to pet the fox. Juan was afraid that it would bite him, but the man said that the animal was very tame. Juan picked the little fellow up in his arms. Holding him close to his body, he stroked the pet's head. At first the fox trembled because he was just as afraid of Juan as Juan had been of him. But soon he stopped trembling and nestled close. Suddenly Juan began to want to keep the fox.

He said to the man, "My father sold his sheep today. He has money. Maybe he will buy this fox if you will sell him."

"Not for forty *pesos* would I sell him. He is my pet. But fifty *pesos* might dry up my sorrow at parting with him," he said, with a twinkle in his eye.

"Fifty *pesos!* There is not so much money in all the world," said Juan, with grief in his voice, as he handed the fox back to the man.

As Juan and Pedro went down the street, Juan said, "Pedro, you know, that man was laughing at me when I gave the fox back to him."

"Yes, of course. He didn't want to sell the fox; so he set a larger price on him than he thought you could pay."

"Well, I wish I could have a pet fox," said Juan.

They turned a corner and saw two boys coming toward them.

"What a big sombrero that boy is wearing!" said Juan, staring.

"Oh," laughed Pedro, "that's not a sombrero. That's a big basket for carrying bread.

82

Juan Delivering Rolls

It fits on the head like a sombrero, but it is full of long rolls. That's Enrique; he is taking them to the restaurant, where he is going to sell them. He and his little brother go there every evening. I know them. Would you like to try the big basket on? Maybe he will let you carry the bread to the restaurant this time."

"Oh, yes, Pedro. That would be fun."

"*¡Hola,* Enrique! This is my cousin Juan, from Parícutin. He has never seen a bread

83

basket like yours. Could he try it on and carry your bread to the restaurant?"

"Certainly," said Enrique.

Juan put the big basket on his head. The other boys laughed while he tried to make it balance. Juan was used to carrying water on his head, but not a big floppy thing like this basket. But he stood very straight and walked along with Enrique's little brother. Soon they reached the restaurant and delivered the bread.

At home, Pedro's mother had prepared a wonderful supper. There were tortillas rolled around ground meat, tamales made of sweet corn meal, and *guacamole* salad of mashed avocado and onion and hot chile peppers. Then there was a huge basket of thin, curled strips of pastry with sugar coating.

The kitchen fascinated Juan. His own mother cooked over an open fire. But Pedro's mother had a big bench covered with red tiles. On top of the bench were little black grills about three feet apart. Along the side of the bench were holes into which she put charcoal, and Juan could see it glowing through the grills.

The house was built around a beautiful patio. In the center of the patio there was a pool of clear water with fish in it. After supper Pedro and Juan played in the patio. Juan chased Pedro along the narrow walks between the flower beds. Pedro leaped over the stepping-stones. Juan was close behind.

Out across the paved yard Pedro ran. Around and around the pool they dashed until Juan felt dizzy. Suddenly Pedro sat down on the wall of the pool and panted hard. Juan dropped down beside him and they laughed. It was so good to have someone to play with. No one in Parícutin played much anymore.

Pedro's mother called to him, "Pedro, you and Juan must pick some fruit for Juan's mother."

"*Sí.*"

The boys took a basket and went out along the narrow walks. There they picked oranges, apples, grapefruit, and lemons from the trees, which were bending over the walks.

Pedro put the fruit into a bag and gave it to Juan to take home to his mother.

Papá was up early the next morning.

"Come, boys!" he called. "We must go home today."

"Papá, I've had such a good time with Pedro," said Juan. "Couldn't we stay just a little longer?"

"No, Juan. We must take home to Mamá the food which Manuel and I bought. Uncle López and Pedro are going home with us to see *el volcán*. They will stay one day with us. So you still have a little time left to play with Pedro."

Juan and Pedro jumped for joy. Hurriedly they collected the things they wished to take with them. Soon Manuel had the wooden saddles on all the little donkeys.

As Juan climbed upon his donkey, he said to Pedro's mother, "Thank you for a wonderful visit."

"Will you come again soon to see us?" she asked.

"Oh, yes, as soon as Papá will bring me. Good-by!"

86

"Good-by, Juan! Good-by, all of you!" she said gaily. "Have a nice journey!"

Juan dreaded to return to the sea of black ash and the roaring mountain. But he wanted to tell his mother all that he had seen. How much he had missed Mamá! The donkeys moved so slowly! If the road to Uruapan seemed to be long, the way back home seemed even longer. He kept his legs swaying constantly, letting them bump against the sides of his stubborn little donkey to make him hurry. Papá and Manuel laughed at him for being in such a hurry.

At last they came in sight of the black cone and the tall plume of the volcano. They could hear faint rumblings. It was a familiar sound. The naked branches of the trees reached up into the summer sky. Not a leaf was to be seen.

"Oh, how terrible!" said Pedro. "I tried to imagine how it would look, but this is worse than I thought it could be."

"Wait," said Juan. "This black blanket isn't

very deep here. Wait till you see how it is piled up at the side of our house. It has already buried us."

When they reached San Juan, they went to see the place where the earthquake had knocked the tower down. Then they went to see Grandfather. Juan told him all about the trip to Uruapan and how brave Pedro had been to walk out on the big pipe over the deep creek. The words tumbled out faster and faster as Juan described his exciting experiences, and his eyes sparkled with pleasure.

All the next day Pedro went from place to place with Juan, as his cousin showed him the volcano and all the wreckage it had caused. How much he would have to tell the ones at home!

4. ▬▬▬▬▬▬▬▬▬▬▬

Juan and the *Turistas*

A FEW NIGHTS after Pedro and Uncle López went home to their lovely city of Uruapan, the strangest thing of all happened to Juan. He was asleep in his bed when the thatched roof fell in, right on top of him!

He screamed, "Papá! Help! Help!" Then he started sobbing.

Papá and Mamá came scrambling through the branches and palm leaves to him and found him nearly buried in ash. The roof had been so deeply covered by ash that it finally had collapsed. Juan wasn't hurt, actually, but he was a badly frightened boy. However, he was out next morning helping Papá put a new thatch on the roof.

After that, Papá had to clean the roof off every few days. The ash fell so fast that it soon became heavy, and this made the roof insecure. Ash had drifted into deep piles around the sides of the house. It was climbing up toward the roof!

The volcano was roaring and erupting constantly now. The ash fell so fast that Papá could not keep the roof from sagging for more than a few hours at a time. Ash was so thick in the air that Juan could scarcely see his hand before his face. Papá was growing weary of fighting ash and hunger and of shoveling out a passageway to the door of his house. The ash had piled so high that now it was more than halfway up the walls.

José's family was nearly choked to death by the dust. Some of his neighbors had finally given up and moved out. One day José came into the house and said to his wife, "María, we move!"

"When, José?" she asked, happy at the thought of freedom from this rain of dust.

"*Mañana.*"

"Why wait until tomorrow?" shouted Juan. "Let's go today."

"No, *mañana.*"

That very afternoon a group of tourists came pouring into town to see the volcano. Juan looked at them in astonishment. He had never seen people with such white skin. He looked at his own brown hands, grimy from the ash and brown from their natural coloring. Then he looked at the white faces.

He asked the visitors how they made their faces so white. But when they spoke to him, he did not understand them. He wondered what their queer talk meant. Turning to Papá, he said, "Papá, why can't I understand them? Why do they have such white faces?"

"Well, Juan, they are North Americans who have come from a far country to see this volcano. They are not brown like you are."

"Farther than Uruapan, Papá?"

"Yes, Juan, much, much farther. They have come from Los Estados Unidos — 'the United States.' It is on the other side of the Rio Grande."

With these visitors were some Mexicans from Mexico City. They told José that they were thirsty. José got water for them, and they

91

drank it, but the Americans would not drink. Juan was puzzled.

"Why won't they drink if they are thirsty, Papá?"

"I don't know."

Then one of the men from Mexico City explained to Papá that the Americans wanted a soft drink from a bottle — soda water, or "Coca Cola." But Papá had nothing to give them.

The men then told Papá that a great many tourists would be coming to see the volcano during the summer. If he set up a stand, he would be able to sell bottled drinks to them and make some money. Papá seemed not to understand how he could do that, but the men said that they would help him arrange everything *mañana* if he decided to do it. Papá agreed. Mamá was very unhappy, because she wanted to move. But Papá always made the decisions. The family always did what Papá thought was best.

The next day the strangers came back with a stand and many different-colored bottles, which Juan looked at with great curiosity.

"Papá, what's in those pretty bottles?" he asked.

"Something North Americans like to drink. You and Manuel are going to sell these drinks to the *turistas.*"

"Papá, it will be fun to sell the drinks, but I cannot talk to the *turistas.* How will I know which color they want?"

"You will learn. They will show you. The men said that the North Americans like their drinks cold. You and Manuel must run to the creek and bring back jugs of cool water to put these bottles in. Soon they will chill."

Juan and Manuel brought the water. In a short while, they found themselves selling these bottled soft drinks to the white-skinned people, who came by the hundreds all summer to see the volcano.

Juan could not understand why anyone would come so far to see anything so terrifying. Although he longed to go away and never see *el monstruo* again, it nevertheless gave him a deep feeling of excitement to watch this big thing growing in his uncle's field and painting the night sky so vividly.

Every day their house became more deeply buried. Then one day the roof caved in. Papá looked at it with disgust and said that he was not going to repair it another time. The family would just live out of doors and sleep under tents like those Juan had seen at the fiesta.

Because other roofs had fallen in, most of the neighbors had moved to San Juan. But in that town, people were having the same troubles. There many roofs were made of tile, but even the tile roofs had begun to sag and cave in. Grandfather was having trouble with his roof. Manuel had had to clean it off many times. With everyone moving away, the town of Parícutin began to seem deserted, and San Juan began to be overcrowded. Even in San Juan the homes had scarcely more than one or two rooms each, but the people were kind enough to take their neighbors in and house them.

José was richer in money now than he had ever been, because these thirsty Americans paid him so much. But now that he had to buy all the food his family ate, he could not keep his money long. However, his family stayed on after most of their neighbors had moved out.

María wanted to go, but José always told her: *"Mañana* we move." Then when *mañana* came, they were still under the shadow of the volcano.

People were calling the volcano Parícutin after the town it was destroying. Many of the Indians still called it simply *"el volcán."* All of them knew what that meant. In their superstitious minds they still regarded it as the work of the Devil, but their first great terror had lessened.

Through the months, Juan and Manuel had grown used to the constant roar and the shower of dust. Even the wonderful fireworks no longer excited them. They went about their daily tasks as usual, scarcely giving the hateful monster more than a glance.

But one day a fearful thing happened. While the boys were sitting at their bottled-drink stand, all the bottles suddenly began to rattle and tumble over. Juan shouted to Manuel, "It's another earthquake!"

A deafening blast came from Parícutin. Manuel jumped up abruptly. "Juan, look at *el volcán!*"

"Oh, Manuel, Parícutin is destroying itself!"

A violent explosion had blown off the top of the cone and had torn one side open. Nearly half of the volcano seemed to be flying through the air. Huge blocks of rock sailed high into the sky. Smaller stones fell far from the cone. Little hot ones were falling on the boys.

"Oh, Manuel, they are coming at us. They burn! Hurry! Let's hide!"

"Where, Juan? There's no place to hide."

Juan looked about him. There was not even a tree left to offer protection.

The two frightened boys huddled by the side of a stack of bottle cases and anxiously watched the sky. Stones were showering the plain, but none of the big ones had come close to them yet.

"Manuel, perhaps Papá was right all along.

Maybe we shall be swallowed up by that monster."

"Not if I can help it!" said Manuel defiantly. "If those stones start falling close, I'm going to run."

"Manuel! Manuel! Look! Parícutin is bleeding!"

From the hole torn in the side of the mountain, a great flood of brilliant flame-colored melted rock, called lava, shot outward like jets of water in a fountain. This was the beginning of the first long river of lava.

The shapely cone, which the volcano had been building all those months, had been ripped and torn apart in those few moments. The molten lava was now free to flow down its sides.

Soon the volcano quieted. Now the river of melted rock gripped the attention of the boys. They saw it gush out and rush toward the base of the cone, and they imagined that soon the whole plain would be flooded with it.

"What do you suppose it can mean, Manuel? What is going to happen now?"

"Juan, surely the Devil is trying to flood

97

us with fire! If we run, maybe we can escape."

The boys sprang to their feet and dashed out across the plain toward San Juan. After awhile, Manuel looked back, and then he stopped. "Juan," he called, "it's not coming so very fast. We're safe now. Let's watch it!"

Juan stopped and sat down with Manuel to watch the lava flow. The brightly glowing river of rock moved steadily until at last it reached the base of the cone. There it slowed and began to spread out. The edges darkened and soon turned to black, slaggy rock that looked like clinkers from a furnace. Escaping gases made the rock look very porous.

Even though it turned to solid rock at the end of the flow, the lava did not stop. On it came. The molten mass pushed the solid crust ahead of it and broke it into huge slabs, which tumbled over and over down the slope.

"Look, Manuel! The rocks are rolling down the hill!" shouted Juan.

All day the boys watched the mass of black rock move down the hill, pushed by the fiery river above it.

After a number of days, the whole mass had

worked its way down to the plain. The boys came often to watch the lava flow. On the mountain was the brilliant river of rock pouring out of the gash in the mountain side. Below was the huge ridge of black spongy lava, or slag, creeping slowly toward the little town of Parícutin. They could go near the ridge now as it crept outward on the plain. It was almost down to some of the little deserted houses.

As the boys walked up close to the ridge, the heat became very great. Several times they approached, only to move back as the heat rushed toward them.

"Manuel, it burns my face. You want to go too close!" exclaimed Juan.

Just then a big slab broke from the black ridge and crashed to the ground close by.

"Come back, Manuel! Come back!" shouted Juan as he ran.

Manuel was already running. Suddenly he stopped and turned to look at the big black ridge.

"Oh, look at that great bright window, Juan!"

At the place from which the slab had fallen there was a brilliant flame-colored patch on the side of the lava flow. A bright mass of lava oozed out and soon changed to black slaggy rock.

"Manuel, its light grows dim. See how fast it darkens! It's black now!" said Juan in wonderment at the strange new sight.

Soon another block broke loose and crashed to the ground. Then another, and another. The boys watched in great excitement as each huge block cracked, leaned, and fell from the big black ridge. A small fragment rolled out near Juan. Cautiously he went to it and put his hand on the ground close by.

"Oh, it's too hot to touch!" he shouted.

Manuel laughed at him.

Juan waited a few minutes. Then he tried again. This time he picked up the fragment, though it was still so hot that he could just barely hold it. He tossed it up and caught it many times before it became cool enough to hold very long.

"Manuel, look at the little sparkles in it! See the pretty colors? On the ridge it looked so black, but it is really covered with little rainbows!" said Juan excitedly.

On the end of the flow the black ash was pushed up into steep cones by the moving ridge. On and on the lava plowed through the ash until it was nearly a mile long!

The summer rains came, fell upon the hot rock, and were turned to steam. This made queer little patches of white clouds all over the flow. What a strange sight! It fascinated the boys. Juan and Manuel would sit by the hour watching the little clouds dance up from the hot rock.

Uncle Dionisio looked sorrowfully at the scene. He believed that God was not going to take the monster out of his field after all. Anyway, there was no field left. In its place was a roaring mountain, which was growing larger every moment.

Even the ruin caused by the birth of the lava flow was quickly healed. Soon the shapely outline was restored to the cone by the falling ash and stones.

But another surprising event took place. Great earthquakes again shook the region as lava burst forth at the base of the cone.

Uncle Dionisio went to see what had happened. Soon he came running back to town, shouting, "Parícutin has a baby born right at its feet!"

Great clouds of dust filled the air again and choked the frightened Indians. And the baby grew and grew. Hundreds of tourists came to see it. Manuel and Juan were very busy selling soda water now. Everyone wanted to see Parícutin's baby, and of course they were thirsty after their long trips.

But when the baby had grown to be four hundred feet high, the eruption ceased. Parícutin was still nearly four times as high as the baby volcano. The tourists began again to give Parícutin most of their attention.

But they showed a great deal of interest in Uncle Dionisio too. He had become the most famous man in the whole countryside. This was because he owned a volcano that was erupting and because he was one of the few men in all the world who had ever seen the birth of a volcano. Hundreds of people questioned him and took careful notes on all that he said. His story of the volcano was printed in papers all over the world.

But in spite of all the publicity, he could not see any real advantage in owning a volcano. In fact, he wished that he didn't have one. He wanted only peace and his cornfield, as it once had been.

Uncle Dionisio would say, "José, I don't like to talk to all these strange people."

"But, Dionisio, you know you never miss the chance," Papá would say.

"Do *you?*" Uncle Dionisio would retort. "Every time you tell the story of the volcano's birth, you make him throw more stones!"

Then Papá and Uncle Dionisio would laugh together.

Papá was becoming well known also, because he had seen all the strange events, too. Of course, since it was Uncle Dionisio's land, he was more famous than Papá.

Uncle Dionisio said, "José, I am weary of this thing. It has ruined my land. It fills my lungs. I have no crops. My family and my animals are hungry. Today a man told me that there was work for me in Texas, the big state just across the Rio Grande, in Los Estados Unidos."

"But, Dionisio, that is so far from us! You would be lonely there."

"You will not stay here much longer either, José. You are stubborn, yes. But you will leave. You will have to leave, because here you will starve. This I know!"

"Maybe you are right, Dionisio," said Papá thoughtfully. Then he asked, "Where will you go in Texas, and what will you do?"

"I shall work in the fields in the Lower Rio Grande Valley," said Dionisio. "Cotton and every kind of vegetable grow there, and the growers need many workers to help cultivate the crops and gather them."

A few days later the river of rock covered a part of the town of Parícutin. The heat from it, as well as the danger that it would cover all the town, became so great that even José no longer could say to María, *"Mañana* we move!" They had to go without delay.

José was forced to pack his few household

belongings on his old broken-down horses and donkeys and move his little family hastily to Grandfather's house in San Juan.

After they had begun to move, Juan looked back at the little deserted town. It seemed so pitiable and lonesome now. Most of the roofs had fallen in under the weight of the ash. The insides of these houses were full of it, and it had piled up to within a foot or two of the tops of the walls. Big tears rolled down Juan's cheek as he turned and trudged on across the plain to San Juan.

Soon after they had moved, the lava ceased to flow. Therefore José kept his stand near the little buried town so that the thirsty Americans might drink and that his family might eat. Juan and Manuel still had to breathe fumes and dust to earn a few *pesos* a day, selling the bottled drinks. But by now they were used to all inconvenience and hardship.

The river of lava had turned to a long rough ridge all the way up to the opening in the

The Town Covered by Lava

mountain side. It lay steaming in the summer
showers — a huge pile of jumbled blocks,
stacked helter-skelter down the whole mile of
its length. Even though it had crusted over,
the inside was still molten. This crust kept
the ridge very hot.

After a time, the blanket of ash began to
bury even the lava flow. Since the ridge was
at least fifteen feet high and many feet wide,
it could not be so easily buried as the little
houses of the Indians had been. But a thick

cover of ash soon was laid upon it, and the ash slowed the cooling. For more than a year, the flow was not to become cold, even at the edges. And all the while those strange little steam clouds danced over its surface — hundreds of them!

Many tourists came in the late afternoon to see the volcano both at sunset and after dark, because it was truly beautiful at those times. Even Juan, who hated it so, found it fascinating. Great billowy clouds of dust, rising many miles into the sky, were gorgeously colored by the setting sun and brilliantly lighted by the lava at night.

No molten lava ever poured from the top of the crater, or opening, of the volcano, but countless red-hot fragments, as well as clots of lava called bombs, shot up into the night sky, making the mountain look like a great fountain of fire. Down the steep sides of the cone these fragments and bombs wove an ever-changing lacework pattern of fiery trails, outlining the cone against the dark heavens. Sometimes, too, great flashes of lightning played through the dust column.

Some of the tourists came to take pictures of the eruption at night. They told Juan that these pictures would be in color — the red glow of the molten rock would show. It was very hard for Juan to imagine how this could be true.

The Americans were thirsty all the time. Even at night Papá and the boys sat with their stand and sold bottled drinks. As the tourists approached, Juan would sing out, "Coca Cola, *bien frío!*"

The Americans always responded to his call. But while they drank, they always grumbled, "*¡Bien frío!* Phooey! This coke has never seen a piece of ice!"

Of course Juan did not understand, but he knew that they were not satisfied. This puzzled him very much. Finally he said, "Papá, North Americans are funny people. They seem to want the drink so much, but when they get it, they never like it."

"Yes, and they come such a distance to see this terrible thing, too. I don't understand them either, Juan. I wish I never had to see it again, but I don't know where to go or what to do to get away from it," said José, with despair in his voice.

When fall came, the American tourists were not so numerous, and the Mexican tourists were not such a thirsty lot as the Americans were.

One day Papá said, "I'm giving up this bottled-drink stand."

"What shall we do for food, Papá?" asked Juan. "We have no crops — it is only the little money from the drinks that buys our food now."

"Well, Juan, I have an idea. You know, those North Americans don't like to walk. Even the Mexican tourists don't like to walk. See how they drag their feet in the ash?"

"It isn't easy to walk in ash, Papá, but of course we are used to it," said Juan.

"Yes, son, but the *turistas* are not. Watch them labor up the ridge! I have a few horses and a few donkeys. Manuel and I can make enough wooden saddles. The *turistas* shall ride. José and his family shall eat!"

A great shout went up from the boys.

109

"You and I shall be their guides," said Papá to them. "We shall walk. All day we shall walk. They will ride. But you shall eat!"

Henceforth little Juan's life was to be very different from what it had been. No car could come past San Juan because of the creeks. Even to San Juan the way was difficult, for there was no road — there were only trails through the woods. The boy would meet the tourists at San Juan and take them to the places they wanted to see. Sometimes he would suggest interesting places for them to visit.

Soon other Indian families began to guide tourists also, and there was much competition among them. Sometimes, however, the parties of tourists were so large that all the guides were needed. At other times there was considerable rivalry among the families. Sometimes men came from Uruapan to make arrangements to have enough horses and donkeys for an especially large party which would arrive in a few days. Then sometimes Papá had to rent horses. This business made much more money for

110

Papá and his family than did the soda water stand. But since Papá had to go all the way to Uruapan to buy everything the family ate, life was still hard.

Gradually Parícutin's eruptions became less violent. As the winter wore on, there were fewer outbursts, and they were more widely spaced. But one never knew what this queer fellow might do. He would lie quietly sleeping for whole days at a time. Then the tourists would be greatly disappointed. Juan would feel sorry for them. After all, they had come a long distance to see the volcano erupt. Then maybe the next day, when they were gone, Parícutin would roar mightier than a lion. He would throw a shower of stones and bombs upon the countryside and fling up a dust curtain five miles high.

The bombs were clots of molten lava which cooled and hardened after they were hurled into the air. They looked like Juan's little clay pig, with its nose and tail drawn out and twisted.

The stones often were huge angular chunks,

111

several feet in width, that had been part of the crust of rock formed between eruptions down in the bottom of the crater. The pressure of the molten rock and that of the expanding gases broke this crust. With great force the fragments were hurled high into the air. Along with them went masses of the molten rock. These cooled and hardened in their trip through the air. At night, they made the fiery trails in the sky and on the sides of the cone. In the daytime, they looked dark as they flew through the air.

Both the bombs and the stones were very dangerous. Many people had narrowly escaped being hit by them. For this reason, the Indians greatly feared them and disliked to go very close to the volcano, even when it seemed to be very quiet.

Papá would say, "Boys, don't take your *turistas* very near *el monstruo*. Tell them that it is very dangerous, for no one knows what he will do. If they insist, take them to our little deserted village. Then say no! Tell them that you are forbidden to go on."

"But, Papá, some get angry and climb

down and walk if we tell them that this is as far as we can go!" said Juan.

"Let them walk! If they get killed, it is not your fault."

At first Juan thought that his new task of guiding the tourists would be more fun than selling bottled drinks. He discovered that it was more interesting, but that it was much harder work. He had to trot many miles each day beside the donkeys and horses. While the animals moved very slowly for the tourists, they moved much too rapidly for the little barefoot boy running along beside them. Sometimes the tourists let Juan climb on behind them and ride, but usually he had to walk.

Then sometimes it rained while they were on trips. Papá had put a large raincape on each saddle, but that was for the tourists. If Juan and Manuel got wet — well, they would soon dry off. No need of raincapes for them!

Sometimes the American tourists were unable to speak Spanish. That, too, made matters very difficult. However, Juan was a gay little boy, and he usually made friends. Most of the Americans had *dulces* and *chicle* to give him, and some of them gave him *propinas,* or tips, in addition to paying Papá for the horses. This was the part which Juan liked. He had never had more than a few *centavos* to put in his clay pig. Now the pig had money in it, and he could buy whatever he wished.

He began to beg all the tourists for tips and became clever about doing it. He liked to get two *pesos* a trip, which was about forty cents. How rich he felt with the coins jingling in his pocket! He always asked, *"Propina por Juan — un peso por Juan, y un peso por Macho."* ("A tip for Juan — one *peso* for Juan and one *peso* for Macho.") Since Macho was the donkey, he could not spend his *peso*. Therefore, Juan had two *pesos* to spend.

Soon Juan learned also that if he could pretend greater danger than there was, he need not go so near the volcano. Then the trip was shorter. The next trip came sooner. There were more *propinas por Juan* and more money in Papá's pocket, and more food in Grand-father's house.

Papá did the bargaining with the tourists at the edge of San Juan. He would go where the other guides gathered to meet the taxicab drivers bringing the tourists from Uruapan. As the tourists stepped from the cabs, the Indians vied with one another for their trade and carried on sharp bargaining with them.

"Twenty-five *pesos* for the donkey!" José would shout.

"No, too much!" the tourists would roar back. "Ten *pesos* for your old, broken-down donkey!"

"No, my donkey would lie down and weep if I let him go for so little."

"What would he do for fifteen?"

"Well, I think maybe he would go for fifteen. A little sulkily perhaps, but he would go," José would respond.

"All right. Fifteen it shall be!"

Everybody was happy, for fifteen *pesos* was what the tourists expected to pay, and it was what José expected to get. Of course he always hoped that the tourists would pay him more, but they seldom did, and he was happy with that amount.

The bargaining was a little game that all the Indians played. Sometimes the tourists did not know how to bargain well, and then the Indians got a larger price for their service.

Another game the Indians learned to play was not so pleasant for the tourists. This game was usually played at night when the big Indians conducted the tours, and the darkness overruled any protests. If the tourists did not specify exactly how far they wanted to go before they took the horses, the guides would take them only about half a mile from San Juan, to a place where the volcano could be well seen, even though it was still three miles away.

Then they would tell the tourists that the way was too dangerous to travel at night for less than fifteen additional *pesos* for each person. They would say that there were deep and treacherous creeks through which one must travel to get to the volcano.

In the daytime, any tourist could have seen that the way lay across a plain cut by a few creek beds, which were deep but usually dry. If he had felt that he was being cheated, he could have dismounted and walked as far as he liked. But at night he had no such choice. He must either pay the extra charge or turn back.

If he protested loudly, the Indians would say, "The donkey has to eat. My family has to eat. We have lost our home. We have lost our sheep, and our cattle, and our fields. You see our situation."

This argument usually won the case. There was nothing more to be said.

5.

Rivers of Lava

SOMETHING DIFFERENT began to happen at Parícutin as the number of eruptions became fewer. On the south side of the volcano, the side away from San Juan, some cracks opened in the ground at the base of the cone. For days the earth shook as the cracks grew wider.

Then the brilliant flame-colored lava rose to the surface and flowed out across the ground. Soon it found the creek beds. Up and up welled the fluid lava, and into the creeks it rushed. It swelled into great fiery rivers of molten rock. Although its temperature was 1900°F., and it was the color of flames, the lava was not actually on fire because real rock, with the exception of coal and sulphur, does not burn.

Down the creeks a short distance the lava began to cool. Then it slowed and began to

118

At the Bocas

move like dough. Still farther down the creeks, it crusted over and turned to a black, slaggy mass. This moved still more slowly. Beneath the crust, the lava remained bright and doughy. The outside became brittle rock, which broke into chunks. These chunks tumbled over one another with a great crunching and grinding sound as the main stream flowed along.

The Indians called the cracks from which the lava flowed *bocas,* or mouths.

119

The *bocas* were forbidden territory for Juan and Manuel. They heard the older Indians telling about the fearful whirlpool of lava where the fiery rock welled up at the sides of the pit, swirled, and then sank out of sight in the center. They heard about the long, brilliant rivers of lava which were filling up the creek beds, swinging around the volcano, and coming right toward the town of San Juan.

"Manuel, why won't Papá let us go to see the *bocas?*" asked Juan.

"Because we should have to go too close to *el volcán*. You can never tell what he is likely to do."

"Manuel, have you seen the *bocas* and the great rivers of lava?"

"No, Papá would not let me go."

"Would you like to go?"

"Of course. Maybe I'll go some day," said Manuel, looking toward the smoking mountain, far away.

"Oh, take me with you when you go," begged Juan.

"No, Juan, that might be a serious matter. Papá said NO! Don't you remember?"

120

"Yes, Manuel," said Juan sadly. "I wish I were big like Papá. Then I'd go. Do you think Papá has been to see the *bocas?*"

"I don't know, but I think so. Papá wouldn't answer that question when I asked him. Just remember that he said it was too dangerous for you to go so close to *el volcán,*" said Manuel.

One day Papá took Manuel with him to get a supply of hay and groceries. He told Juan to take Macho and try to hire him out to a tourist. Juan glowed with pride to think that he was going to do the bargaining that day. Since the tourists had to have a way of transportation, the little boy felt sure that he could earn a pocketful of *pesos.*

He played ball with the other little Indians until he saw a car plowing through the deep black ash. Then he ran like a deer to be with the men when the bargaining began. He untied his donkey and brought it up to the car.

Some of the grown men rudely pushed him aside and stepped up to the large, handsome

121

American tourist who was getting out of the taxicab.

"Thirty *pesos* for this fine horse!" they said.

In perfect Spanish, the American told him that the price was too much.

"Veinte pesos por Macho (Twenty *pesos* for Macho)!" called Juan from behind the big Indian.

Another man pushed him aside and called, "Twenty-five *pesos* for my horse!"

"Let's see what the boy has," said the American.

"Not that tired old donkey for a big North American!" said the first Indian scornfully, waving Juan and Macho away.

"Macho is a fine donkey. He can go anywhere," said Juan.

"But twenty *pesos* is too much for any of your animals. I can walk," said the American.

Then he looked at Juan again and said, "How about ten *pesos?*"

"No, *señor*. Macho would be insulted. He would put his ears back and sit down. He would not go for less than fifteen *pesos*."

The American laughed and said, "All right

122

— fifteen *pesos* it shall be. But mind you, I'm going to the volcano. None of this monkey business of getting out half a mile from the village and then bargaining for more money. Does that suit you? Is it an agreement?"

"Yes, *señor,*" said Juan, his face showing pride that he had beaten the big Indians at bargaining.

Then the American turned to the two big Indians, who seemed disappointed, and said, "Next time don't push the little fellow around."

Then he climbed up on Macho. His legs were so long that his feet nearly touched the ground. Juan trotted alongside the donkey, easily keeping pace with Macho's plodding steps.

"What is your name?" asked the American.

"Juan."

"Well, Juan, you may call me Bill."

"All right. Is this the first time you have seen Parícutin, Bill?"

"Oh, no. I've been here before. I come

123

often to see what goes on at that old smoke-stack. It's very interesting to me. You see, Juan, I'm a geologist. Do you know what that is?"

"No."

"Well, I study the earth and the rocks that make the earth. That's why I have this hammer and collecting bag. When I come back from Parícutin, Macho is going to have a much heavier load than he has now because I'll have half of *el volcán* in this bag. I take pictures of the old fellow's fireworks too. That's why I have these cases. My cameras are in them."

"Why do all the Americans come here to see Parícutin? Is this the only volcano in the world?"

"Oh, no, Juan. There are thousands of volcanoes. In fact, there are thousands of them right here in Mexico. All these little flat-topped hills around this plain were once active volcanoes. They are asleep now. Maybe they will never awaken again."

"Well, then, if there are so many volcanoes, why do North Americans come so far to see this one?"

"Juan, there are really only about four hundred and fifty active volcanoes in the world today. All the rest are either extinct or dormant."

"What's that — 'dormant'?"

"Well, if a volcano is 'extinct,' it is no longer active. If it is 'dormant,' it is asleep. Someday it will erupt again. We cannot always tell which is the case. Sometimes when we think a volcano is extinct, it is only dormant."

"What makes a volcano, Bill? Papá says it is hell opening up."

Bill laughed. "Oh, no, Juan. There are simply places where deep cracks form in the earth. That lets molten lava come to the surface, if there is any present beneath the ground."

"Is the lava everywhere under the ground?"

"Geologists don't think so. They think that it is found where movements are taking place in the outer part of the earth, and that it finds cracks and weak places and forces its way to the surface, where it erupts.

"There are several reasons why we North Americans are so very much interested in Parícutin. In the first place, we have only one active volcano in the United States. He is a lazy fellow, and he sleeps most of the time. So if we want to see an active volcano, we must go outside of the country.

"Then, there is only one other volcano whose birth was seen by man. So, of course, we don't know much about the early stages of volcanoes. That is why Parícutin is so important to us. We want to watch it grow."

"I was there when Parícutin was born, right in Uncle Dionisio's cornfield!" said Juan excitedly.

"Oh, so you saw the 'blessed event,' did you?"

"What's that? We think it is a curse, not a blessing, to us."

"To be sure, it was no blessing to you. That's just a way of speaking of a baby's birth."

Juan and Bill laughed. Then Bill asked, "How loudly did he yell when he was born?"

"He roared, and he rumbled, and he threw up a great cloud of white smoke and black dust, and then he began to throw stones at the sun."

"A strong fellow, wasn't he?"

"We were scared. I trembled like wind in a tree. Mamá went down on her knees and began to pray. Papá just stood and stared, with his mouth open. But soon we all began to run because the stones were falling too close to us. And the heat was very great."

"Well, Juan, you've seen what any geologist would give his eyeteeth to see."

"You North Americans seem to love Parícutin so much, but we Indians don't like him. He has caused us great suffering. He has ruined our homes and has made us hungry. We have had to work very hard because of him."

"Yes, it has certainly been a hardship. But didn't you get a big thrill 'way down inside of you when you saw that fellow grow to be one hundred and twenty feet high in the first day of his life?"

"No, I was too frightened."

"Well, after you were not frightened any-more, didn't you get a thrill out of watching him grow? Why, he's just a little over a year and a half old now, and he is fifteen hundred feet high already. Just think of it! Just think of the power and force that have gone into making him so big. And think of the golden and rosy beauty of his plume at sunset! Boy, don't you get the thrill of your life watching him shoot fireworks at night?"

"Of course! I do think he's beautiful and exciting, but he makes me sad because I think grass and trees are beautiful too. Look! Where do you see grass? It's summer, but would you know it? Is there one green leaf on that tree? Look at that cornfield! I can remember seeing it wave in the wind. Now just stubble sticks up through the ash. Everywhere there's ash, ash, ash! No sheep, no cows, no chickens, no fruit. We don't have good things to eat anymore, either."

"That side of it has been very hard, I know, Juan, but sometimes one wonder of nature kills another. There are other fields. You can make your home elsewhere. But always remember *el volcán* as the one great wonder of your life. You have seen what probably no other little boy has seen since recorded history — a volcano being born!

"You have watched him grow. You have seen him paint the sunrise. You have seen him

128

when he was young blow his top off and split his side wide open. You have seen him bleed a river of lava and then heal himself and grow again. See how graceful he is — his sides so steep and smooth and even, his top so flat, with that great billowy cloud curling out of his crater! Isn't he beautiful, Juan? Wonder at him, but don't be bitter at him. He couldn't help being born any more than you or I."

"I know it, but I still don't like him. Look there, Bill. See that little square mound. See the plaster wall just sticking above the ground? That's the top of the house where I used to live. Here's where I used to play. And over there is where Macho used to sleep. It's all ash now."

Juan's big brown eyes were full of tears as he looked up at Bill.

"Here, Juan, get up on this donkey. I know you must be tired. You've had a hard life, poor kid! First, a volcano; then an invasion of American tourists. But remember what I said. Parícutin may be terrible, but he is wonderful too. You don't have to like him, but don't forget his beauty and the marvel of his coming and his growth. That's what makes life interesting and happy."

They passed the crumbling walls of the old church in the little buried town of Parícutin and slowly walked down to the first lava flow. Little patches of white vapor were rising from its ash-covered surface.

"It looks as if that old lava flow is never going to cool off," said Bill. "I'll bet there are some fancy minerals in the holes. Let's have a look."

"¡Cho, Macho!" called Juan.

The donkey came to a halt as Bill and Juan slid to the ground.

Bill found a good-sized cavernous opening between large blocks of lava. It was roofed by ash and slaggy lava. Inside, where the rain water had trickled through, it had dissolved minerals from the lava. These had been deposited again on the walls of the little cave. Also gases from the interior of the flow had crept toward the surface, carrying with them minerals of various sorts. All these minerals formed a crystalline crust over the walls.

Taking out a flashlight, Bill flashed a beam around the inside of the cavity. The crystals glistened like a million diamonds. Some were pure white, some were golden-yellow, and some were greenish.

"Look at that, Juan. Who would expect to see such beauty in an ugly old black lava flow? But there it is — shining!"

"Truly, it is very beautiful!" said Juan.

"See what I mean? Parícutin is not all bad, eh? And you are not still afraid of him, are you?"

Juan grinned and shook his head. Just then his bare foot sank into the ash and on down into a little hot cavity. He yelled and jumped like a frog.

"Watch out, Juan! I don't want roasted feet for lunch today. I have something a lot better. Do you like chicken? Which piece do you want for your lunch, the drumstick or the pulley bone?"

Juan felt like crying because the ash had burned his foot, but the prospect of having

131

chicken for lunch was so exciting that he forgot the foot and nearly shouted for the drumstick.

"All right. Just wait until I chip off a few samples of these crystals; then we'll go over to the shade and see what I have in the lunch box. Wow! This ash is so hot it burns right through my shoes!"

"Oh, it is very hot," said Juan, "but my foot doesn't hurt so much now. At least, I haven't time to think about the burn. I want to start thinking about that chicken."

"That's the spirit, boy! Have fun even if your foot burns; even if a volcano grows in your fields instead of corn," said Bill.

Juan had liked all the American tourists, but none so well as Bill. This American was simply wonderful, and, what was more, he had chicken in his lunch box!

When Bill had put the crystals into the collecting bag, the two climbed onto Macho and turned toward the volcano again.

"That looks like a nice shady spot up the ravine by the ridge," said Bill, pointing to the sloping foot of an old volcano that stood be-

132

side the new one. "We can eat there, and then we'll have the energy to climb that ridge. It wouldn't be fair to make Macho carry us both up that steep slope — us with dinners under our belts and Macho yearning for the green fields that are gone.

"Juan, let me tell you something else to make you feel better. This country all looks bare and unfriendly to plants now. But you wait — the rains soaking down through this ash will do a marvelous thing. One day the soil will be rich, and grass will grow greener here than you have ever seen it grow before. Of course, it will take a number of years. I can't say how long, but with all the rain that comes down here every summer afternoon, it won't be too long before the ash turns to soil."

"Will Parícutin still be erupting then?"

"Maybe not. He is already slowing down. This kind of volcano usually lasts only a few weeks or, at most, a few years. It is what we call a cinder cone. It probably will not grow much higher, but it may grow larger around.

"There are thousands of this kind of volcano in this part of the world. They lie in a broad belt, stretching across Mexico, from the Gulf of Mexico to the Pacific Ocean. This zone forms the southern border of the plateau of Mexico. To the north of us, the land is high and generally flat. To the south of us, it is hilly but generally lower."

"Bill, are there bigger volcanoes than Parícutin?"

"Oh, yes, Juan. Along this belt there are some very high volcanic mountains. One is over eighteen thousand feet high. These high peaks are a different type of volcano from this one. They are shaped differently. See how straight the sides of Parícutin are? See how flat his top is and how broad it is? The sides of the big cone curve in. They have bases many miles across, and they have very narrow tops. They are made of many layers of lava between layers of cinders. It takes thousands of years for them to grow because they don't erupt very often — maybe just once in a hundred years."

"Are there very many of these big volcanoes, Bill?"

"Yes, over the world there are a lot of them. Here in Mexico there are many more of the

134

small cinder cones, which have more ash and cinder than lava in their cones. Each of these little ones grew up in the space of a few weeks, or perhaps a few years, and then ceased to erupt. Right now Parícutin seems to be of this type. But one never knows. It is possible for him to grow into a long-lived cone, like the famous 'Popo' near Mexico City. The *bocas* and the rivers of lava at its base make me wonder if this is not just the beginning of a great cone like Popo."

"Papá said a man told him that there was a smoking mountain called Popo. Does Popo ever throw stones like Parícutin does?"

"Yes, but it has been a long time since he has erupted."

They rode up a small ravine between the ridge and the lava flow and found a shady place to eat. Juan had never tasted such wonderful food as Bill had in his lunch. And there was so much of it.

"This will give us strength to get up over the ridge so that we can go on around this volcano to the *bocas*," said Bill, when all the food had disappeared.

"To the *bocas!*" exclaimed Juan. "I can't go there."

"What are you afraid of, Juan? Of course they are mouths, but they don't bite. They would swallow you up if you jumped in, but who's that crazy?"

"But I just can't go there," he protested. "Macho can't go there either."

"Of course he can, and so can you," said Bill. "Am I going to have to pick both you and Macho up and carry you? Have you ever seen the *bocas*, Juan?"

"No," said Juan, with his eyes as wide as saucers.

"Look, Juan, I've seen the *bocas*, and I'm still alive. I don't see what you are afraid of."

"Oh, I'm not afraid of the *bocas*, but I am afraid to go close to Parícutin. I know what he can do. Just listen to him roar! Once I took a lady too close, and he threw a big stone at her, and it hurt her leg."

"So you don't believe in annoying a volcano, eh? Well, look, Juan, he *is* treacherous, but

136

right now he isn't kicking up a very big fuss; and lots of people have moved about safely under his shadow."

"We Indians don't trust him."

"You should see the *bocas*. They are the most wonderful part about Parícutin now. Why, most boys would give anything to get the chance to see such a marvelous sight, and here you live right beside the *bocas* and have never seen them. Don't you have the least little bit of curiosity?"

"Oh, yes, I do have curiosity!" exclaimed Juan.

"Well, then, what are you afraid of?"

"Papá."

"So that's it! Well, of course you can't go there alone, but I'll take the place of your father and go with you. That will be all right with him, won't it?"

"I guess so," said Juan, rather doubtfully. Then he looked serious and said, "Suppose I get killed?"

"Well, Papá can't spank you then!"

Juan laughed, and Bill said, "Let's go, then.

We have to get to those *bocas* before the afternoon rains start."

They began the slow, hard climb up the ash-covered ridge, Juan tingling with excitement. The ash was many feet deep, and it was loosely laid. At each step, they slid back almost as much as they went forward.

After about ten minutes of puffing, they came out on the flat which had once been the basin where Dionisio raised corn. Here they stopped for a rest before they climbed upon Macho again.

In front of them, about a quarter of a mile away, stood the tall, smooth cone of Parícutin. Above their heads towered the dun-colored plume, billowy and beautiful in the noonday sunlight. A heavy shower of dust and ash was falling beside the cone just ahead of them.

"I hate to go through all that dust," said Bill, "but there's no way out of it if we are to get to the *bocas,* because this old volcano beside Parícutin keeps us from making a wider swing around the mountain. Goodness! Parícutin is a stinker!"

"What makes him smell so?" asked Juan.

"Most people think that it is sulphur. But scientists, who have studied these gases carefully, say that he doesn't give off sulphur vapors. It is a mixture of other fumes. Whatever they are — well, he's no rose."

"Listen," said Juan. "He's growling at us."

"Noisy fellow, isn't he?"

Suddenly Parícutin rumbled violently and shook the ground. Then up shot a shower of stones. Most of them fell back into the crater. Some of them tumbled down the mud-streaked side of the cone, and a few fell clear of the cone just several hundred yards ahead of Juan and Bill.

"See, that's why we Indians are afraid to go too close. It makes Parícutin angry. He wants us to stay away."

"Nonsense!" said Bill. "Of course we talk about the volcano as though it were alive, but it really isn't. Only man and other animals can have feelings and emotions. Parícutin can't get angry, like a person. Come on, let's get onto Macho and get started."

As they mounted Macho, Bill looked up again at Parícutin. The long whitish mud streaks which ran down the side of the cone were cut by a thin gray diagonal line which curved around the cone from the base to the top.

"Juan, do you see that line?"

"Yes."

"I was one of the crazy guys who helped make it. I climbed the cone a couple of times several weeks ago with a group of Mexico City boys. Those were some climbs! At every step we seemed to slide back farther than we went up.

"Then, one of the times, when the wind was just right, the dust and fumes swept down over us. They very nearly choked us to death and almost buried us. Parícutin was not very active that day, but because we were on the side of the cone, he seemed to be erupting violently. It was really terrifying. Every now and then there were showers of stones. They were very hot. Most of them were just rolling down the side of the cone, but they were coming so fast that we danced like grasshoppers to dodge them. You would have split your sides laughing at us when we were trying to take

140

moving pictures of one another doing the grass-hopper leap over the showers of stone."

"Did you go all the way up?"

"Not that time. We just couldn't make it. We got about three quarters of the way up, but the showers of dust and stones, as well as the fumes, finally defeated us.

"The next time we climbed the cone, the volcano was completely quiet. We went up to the top that time."

"Oh, you were *very* brave! Any moment he might have filled the sky with stones! You never know what he is going to do. He sleeps a long time; then suddenly he roars, and up comes a shower of stones! You have to be brave to climb him!" said Juan.

"Brave or *loco*," laughed Bill. "I guess I was a little bit of both, but I wanted to see what was up there in the crater. What I saw were a deep pit and many big chunks of hardened lava scattered around. Everything was covered with black ash. The fumes were suffocating. I took some pictures; then we hustled back down the cone.

"Last week I flew over the crater in an airplane and took pictures. That was more fun and much easier."

"It must have been very exciting!" said Juan.

"Nothing else was so exciting as our grass-hopper dance. We were very lucky not to get hurt by those stones. Well, Juan, we are nearly to the *bocas* now. Get ready for the sight of your life."

In a moment they stood on the brink of a great pit of flame-colored lava, which was churning around, spouting up here and there.

"This is the whirlpool, Juan."

Juan was breathless with excitement. Before him lay a huge yawning basin full of swirling and bubbling lava. He broke a limb from a dead tree near by and cautiously stepped to the brink of the whirlpool. The lava nearly blinded him, and the heat almost seared his face, but he managed to stick his branch into the lava and bring it up flaming. He turned to Bill and laughed.

"You see, Juan, that stuff isn't burning like your stick. It is just terribly hot."

Juan threw the stick into the pool. It

flamed up, swirled momentarily with the lava, and then sank out of sight in the center of the pit.

They went on to other large cracks from which the lava issued and flowed out into the creeks. There they threw in stones to test the speed of the flow.

"As nearly as I can figure it, Juan, the lava seems to be flowing about a hundred feet a minute up here near the cracks."

Downstream it ran more slowly and changed to the doughy appearance. Where it began to thicken, great blocks of brilliant orange-colored lava were pushed up in the flow. These would split apart and then slump gradually down into the flow just as a mass of rising dough might ease over the side of a pan. They stood for a long time watching the peculiar movement. Bill took pictures with both his cameras.

They went farther downstream and watched the lava turning to slag and crusting over. Big blocks broke from the crust and sank into the brilliant mass of lava. Sometimes these blocks would bob up and tumble over other blocks with grinding, crunching, and crashing sounds. On downstream a jumbled mass of black slag stretched as far as they could see. Here and there a window would open up as a block fell, and bright lava would peek through at the daylight. But it turned black as it cooled.

Bill said, "Juan, it doesn't take much cooling to turn that stuff to hard, black rock. While it is melted, its temperature is 1900°, which is nine times as hot as boiling water! When it cools to 1850°, it is black rock. Of course, in such a big mass, it takes months to cool enough so you can handle it."

Juan looked as though he did not understand what Bill was telling him. So Bill said, "Come on, let's go over to the canyon. I have something to show you."

There was a canyon near by which was about one hundred feet deep. One of the rivers of lava flowed into it and made a lava falls. Bill and Juan worked their way down the canyon wall and up the other side. It was a rough

144

climb, but they made it. Juan puffed as he scrambled from ledge to ledge, but he was so filled with the spirit of adventure that it seemed as if he could almost climb a sheer cliff.

When they were on top of the canyon wall, Bill said, "Now look at that lava."

"Oh, that is the most beautiful sight I have ever seen!" Juan exclaimed.

In front of them was a steep cliff nearly a hundred feet high. The lava flow had floated a huge boulder of solid lava to the brink of the canyon. There it had become lodged. The lava stream divided and flowed around it in two brilliant bands down the cliff, and then these met to form a V on the canyon wall.

Bill took his pictures. The two adventurers stood long in silent admiration. Finally, Bill looked up and saw a huge thunderhead cloud piling up into a billowy white cauliflower-like mass overhead.

"Look, kid, we have to start back. Climbing out of that canyon in the rain won't be any fun. If we didn't have Macho, we'd just swing on down this creek, but we'll have to go back to him. Have you had fun?"

"Oh, yes, Bill! This has been the most wonderful day of my life!"

"Do you think the trip was well worth the risk of a spanking?"

"Sure," giggled Juan. "Papá won't spank me since I was with you."

"Well, I wouldn't have brought you if I had thought there was serious danger."

"I'm glad I came with you because the *bocas* are wonderful, and I like the lava falls. I like you, too," said Juan.

"Well, thank you, fellow. I like *you*. In fact, I like you so well that I am going to give you ten *pesos* just for yourself, and I'm going to give Macho five extra *pesos*. You can take care of Macho's money for him."

"Oh, thank you, Bill. That's more money than I've ever had!"

"Yes, maybe. But now don't be silly and spend it foolishly. If you spend it, buy something you need."

"I'll put it in my little painted pig, which Grandfather gave me, and save it."

146

The Lava Flow

Juan was so happy that he felt as though he were floating down the canyon wall. When he started up the other side, however, he was sure he was not floating. It was a steep, hard pull. But the thought of fifteen *pesos* did make the climb easier.

When he had reached the top, he ran to Macho and whispered the good news in his ear, *"Propina por Juan y Macho —* ten *pesos* for Juan and five *pesos* for Macho."

Macho flopped his long ear against Juan's

147

nose, and Juan giggled as he jumped back to help Bill load the saddle with his bags and cameras.

"Well, we are off again. Let's see if we can beat that rain back to San Juan. Say, I forgot something! Here's that fifteen *pesos*. It might be safer to give it to you now, because if I wait to pay you at San Juan, somebody might relieve you of the money."

Juan chuckled. *"Muchas gracias,"* he said gratefully.

Macho brought them safely back before the afternoon rains came. His ears churned around and around constantly as he plodded along the ash-covered ground. Such a dull life for a donkey — not even one spear of grass to make things interesting! Macho snorted his disgust.

At home they found José waiting for them. Bill gave him fifteen *pesos*. "Fine boy you have there. And a good donkey too!" said Bill to José.

"Thank you, *señor*," said José.

148

"I'll see you next time," Bill called to Juan as he got into his taxicab.

"Good-by, Bill!"

Juan turned to José and said, "Papá, he was wonderful. He gave me lunch and fifteen extra *pesos*. I would like to give you half of it to buy us more food, and I would like to save half of it."

José smiled with pride at his son. "Save it all, Juan. Maybe some day we shall need food more than we need it today. Manuel and I bought a fine supply this morning. You were gone a long time, Juan. What kept you so long?"

"Papá, the man studies rocks. He spent much time collecting rocks and beautiful crystals in the old lava flow. Then he took pictures of the *bocas* and the lava falls. He says he'll take me with him on the next trip that he makes. He's the best North American I've ever seen."

Just then Macho brayed.

Juan said, "See, Papá, Macho agrees with me!"

Papá did not say anything for a moment.

Juan waited tensely for a response. Finally Papá said slowly, to himself, "Fifteen extra *pesos!*" To Juan he said, "You'd better go feed Macho."

That night Juan dreamed of Bill and the *bocas* and the beautiful lava falls — and fifteen *pesos*.

6.

Adiós, Parícutin

ALL THROUGH the summer months, tourists still came by the hundreds to see the volcano. Each day Manuel and Juan trotted beside their donkeys to guide the tourists through the creeks and across the plain. Each day José's pocket grew fat with money. He had never seen so much money in all his life. But now José had no field in which to raise food, and he had no sheep or cattle, or even chickens. For the first time, he had to buy everything for his family.

How fast the money disappeared! Each week he emptied his purse at the market, and still his children were hungry. Even if he had had enough money, there was not enough food for everybody.

151

José would stand in the doorway of Grandfather's house, shake his head, and look bitterly at Parícutin. He would think of the peaceful days when he used to till his own cornfield and help his neighbors with theirs. But he no longer prayed that Parícutin be removed. All his prayers now were for San Juan. San Juan lay in the path of destruction.

Through the months the rivers of lava had slowly crept toward this town. They were more than four miles long now — great black tongues of lava, stretching out across the plain, winding through the creek beds, and bearing down upon San Juan.

José would say to Grandfather, "What do you suppose we have done to bring this curse upon us?"

"I don't know, son," Grandfather would answer. "We have observed all the saints' days. We have prayed. What more could we do? I do not know why this came to us. But I shall keep on praying that the lava will not cover our home. All my life I have lived here. I intend to die here. I won't move!"

"If we did want to move, where could we

go?" said Papá. "Of course Dionisio went to Texas. Some men there gave him work. But no one has given me work. I don't know where to go."

Over and over, day after day, Juan heard them talking in this way. He remembered that Papá had said he would not leave the village of Parícutin. Then the lava had come there, and Papá had moved. Would Grandfather move if the lava came? Grandfather was so very stubborn! The great rivers of lava were coming closer to San Juan every day now. The little boy trembled at the thought. Where would they go if they had to leave?

It had been a year and a half since Parícutin was born, but only a few months since the rivers of lava had begun to flow from its base. Although they flowed very rapidly out of the *bocas,* they moved very slowly at the end of the flow — sometimes twenty feet an hour; at other times, only a foot or so an hour. Their sides and ends caved off and crashed to the ground. The molten interiors pushed on over the fallen slabs. More fell. On moved the

153

mass, foot by foot. All the flows seemed to be coming upon San Juan at once.

At last, they were at the very edge of the town. Everyone had watched the flows anxiously, praying. But on they came, never stopping, creeping day and night. Soon the great spongy slabs of slag came crashing into a yard. In a few minutes, they tumbled against the house. For a moment a huge window opened in the lava flow. From this opening oozed a doughy mass of orange-colored molten lava, which pushed against the house. Instantly the house was in flames. On moved the huge black mass, right over the burning house and into the next yard. On across the helpless town it went.

Reluctantly each Indian family moved out as the big ridge of lava threatened its home. The remaining houses were already crowded with refugees from the village of Parícutin. The new victims had no place to go except to the plaza. There they either set up tents or slept under the stars. At night they could see the red glow of Parícutin's fireworks, and

154

they could hear the crashing lava pushing toward the plaza. They knew that again they must move out of its path.

Where once the light-hearted youths had marched to choose their sweethearts at fiestas, there was now only the bleak desolation of black ash. Along the streets, tired old roofs sagged under the weight of it. Some had even fallen in.

Soon it became plain that the whole town was doomed to destruction. But stubbornly the Indians clung to their homes as long as they could.

As the lava came closer to his home, Grandfather's voice became louder as he said defiantly, "I am not going to move! San Juan is my home. I was born here, and I expect to die here!"

He would stand silent for hours, watching the slow progress of the lava flow. Then suddenly he would scream at it, "I won't move!"

Then he would calm down. He would shake his head and stroke his white beard. Juan was worried about what Grandfather would really do when the lava came upon his

155

house. For even Juan knew that Grandfather's house would surely be destroyed. The lava kept moving, burning one house after another, and covering the ashes as it swallowed the next house. Sometimes a house would be passed by one flow, only to be surrounded by another and cut off.

Soon the Indians began to realize that not even their old church was to be spared. To them this seemed even worse than losing their homes. They had always thought of the church as their protection. Now, not only was it to suffer the disaster of having one of its towers shaken to the ground, but it was also about to suffer total destruction! It lay right in the path of three lava flows. Slowly the flows crept against the stone wall, pressing it from the back and from the sides. The front still bravely faced the plaza. The walls held. This was the first man-made thing to withstand the terrible pressure of the lava for even a short while.

Juan watched it slowly pile against the great stone walls. Then he ran home to Grandfather.

"Oh, Grandfather! Come quickly! The old

church is lost! The lava is pouring into its windows!" he shouted.

There were tears in Grandfather's eyes. Grandmother was on her knees, holding her rosary.

"I don't want to see it, son. It makes my heart ache!" said Grandfather.

Juan ran back to the plaza. He saw the priest and some of the villagers rushing in and out of the church frantically. They were carrying out the art treasures and the furnishings of the church. Donkeys were waiting at the door to be loaded. A long line of donkeys was moving slowly down the street, carrying the precious objects to safety.

The lava piled higher against the church. It climbed to the roof and flowed about the sides. A wall finally gave way, and into the church crashed the rivers of lava! Soon the whole church was filled with huge blocks of black slag. The roof fell in, and the walls were pushed out. The lava moved on, leaving only the one tower, standing like a lighthouse above a sea of black slag.

On out across the plaza the ugly mass flowed.

On down the street it crept, crushing, splintering, and burning the houses in its path.

At last most of the Indians were resigned to the destruction. If even the House of God could not be saved from ruin, what hope had they that their homes would be spared? At last some of them began to tear down their homes before the lava could destroy them. Board by board they moved them to the village of Anghaua, which was several miles to the east. There, along the creek flats, they stacked their lumber in neat piles to await the day when they would rebuild their homes in this town.

The army came with big trucks and moved some of the families. Some few refused to go. They still hoped and believed that a miracle would save them. Others, like José, postponed the day of moving because they were too busy with the hundreds of tourists who came to look upon their misfortune and to watch Parícutin erupt. This meant money in José's pocket.

At last José and Grandfather were faced with the necessity of moving, for the lava flow

158

was coming right upon their homes. As the family began to gather their belongings together, Grandfather still said, "I won't move!" But no one paid any attention to him now. Juan was still worried about Grandfather, but he was so busy loading the donkeys that he could not stop to talk to the old man.

Load after load went to Anghaua. Then everyone but Grandfather helped with the tearing down of the house. The plaster was knocked off. The frame was torn apart. Some of the boards were loaded upon the donkeys. José and Juan made several trips to Anghaua with the boards, but they could not carry them fast enough. The lava was coming too rapidly now to take the chance involved in having the donkeys move the lumber out. Instead, each member of the family picked up a few boards and started afoot to Anghaua.

Juan said, "Come on, Grandfather, let's go quickly before the lava comes!"

Grandfather did not say a word. He just got on his little donkey and rode slowly away with the family.

Mamá and Grandmother wept as they

trudged along over the black blanket of ash with the boards under their arms. Their heavy burdens grew heavier, but on and on they struggled.

Of course, Grandfather rode instead of letting his donkey carry boards. He felt that the burden in his heart was as great as all the burdens in their tired arms. He was being forced to leave his birthplace and all the familiar places he had learned to love so dearly during his long life.

It was late summer, but not a blade of grass, not a flower, not a green leaf could be seen — only a black sheet of ash on everything. Although the sun was very hot upon them, the countryside looked as if winter had already come and had destroyed all the plant life. Certainly winter had settled in upon their hearts.

Along the trail there were other Indians, trudging barefooted through the ash and carrying their poor possessions to new homes. Some, like José's family, were making their second journey. It was a sad little band of refugees. Many were weeping.

As they climbed up a little hill, Juan turned for a last look at San Juan. There stood the tall white church tower in the sea of black rock. A few homes had escaped destruction, for they were not in the paths of the lava flows as they turned westward to move on down the plain past the town. Some of the long tongues now stretched far beyond San Juan. They were nearly seven miles long!

A big tear rolled down Juan's cheek. He raised his eyes to the horizon. There stood Parícutin, smoking lazily in the morning sunlight, with its long plume of dun-colored dust curling high into the sky. He remembered Bill's words. Turning to Papá he said, "I don't like that old volcano. He makes me very unhappy. But he is beautiful."

Papá grunted.

Then Juan said to Grandfather, "There are other fields. We can make our home somewhere else, Grandfather."

Grandfather's head drooped. His white beard rested on his chest. He rode on in silence.

Epilogue

AFTER JUAN and his family were forced to make their second move, the rivers of lava covered most of the town of San Juan de Parangaricutiro. A few houses were left standing, and their owners clung to them until the lava flows threatened to surround them.

The *bocas* continued to pour out lava for years after Juan's family moved. The early flows started on the south, flowed northward around the east side of the cone, and eventually turned westward through San Juan. Then one day a flow arose on the south side of the volcano and moved around the other side of the mountain down the route taken by Juan and Bill. Between Parícutin and the old volcanic cone it flowed. On down the slope it crept until at last it covered every sign of the tiny town of Parícutin with a sheet of black rock.

Up and up piled the lavas around the cinder cone until the lava flows very nearly buried it.

Meanwhile Parícutin went on erupting now and then, scattering dust over the countryside. For nine years in all, it painted the night sky with fireworks, and for more than eight years, rivers of lava poured from its base. Then in the spring of 1952, just when some scientists had worked out a plan to use the heat of the lavas to make electric power, the lavas ceased to come, and Parícutin no longer painted the sunrise with his rosy plume.

All has been quiet above the black blanket of ash for a year. It is thought that Parícutin is extinct. He may be just dormant. Who knows? He served the scientists well. They learned much from him. Even though he ruined homes and fields, even though he made Juan and his family unhappy, he brought much wealth to Mexico. Many a foreigner came just to see the marvel of the volcano. The *turista* left his money in exchange for serapes, *huaraches, cestas, tazas,* donkey rides, and all manner of things. He left Mexico richer, and he went home richer too, for he carried with him the memory of the smoking mountain and the great rivers of lava; the memory of a gentle, courteous people; the memory of the beauty and magnificence that is Mexico.

Now that all is quiet in Michoacán, other and more silent earth forces are busily at work in the sea of black ash and rock. They will turn the rock to rich soil — richer than ever before. One day new cornfields will grow where others were buried. Bill was right — Parícutin is not all bad.

Glossary

adiós (ä-dĕ-ōs'), good-by

bien frío (bē-ĕn' frē' ȯ), ice cold

boca (bō' cȧ), mouth

caballo (cä-bä' yȯ), horse

canasta (cä-näs' tȧ), large basket, hamper, crate

centavo (sĕn-tä' vȯ), cent

cesta (sĕs' tȧ), small basket

chicle (chē' clĕ), chewing gum

chile (chē' lĕ), red pepper

¡cho! (chō), whoa!

cinco (sēn' cȯ), five

Dionisio Pulido (dē' ȯ-nē' sĕ-ȯ pōō-lē' dȯ), Dennis Pulido

dulces (dōōl' sĕs), candies

Estados Unidos de América (ĕs-tä' dȯs ōō-nē' dōs dä a-mä' rĕ-cȧ), United States of America

fiesta (fyĕs' tȧ), holiday or festival

figurita (fē' gōō-rē' tȧ), figurine

gracias (grä' cē-ȧs), thanks, thank you

guacamole (gwä' cȧ-mō' lĕ), salad of avocado, onion, and seasoning

¡hola! (ō' lȧ), hello!

huarache (wä-rä' chĕ), sandal

jícara (hē' cä-rȧ), chocolate cup

José (hō-sä'), Joseph

Juan (hwän), John

loco (lō' cȯ), crazy, foolish

Macho (mä' chȯ)

mamá (mä-mä'), mama

167

Manuel (män-wĕl´), Emanuel

María (m*a*-rē´ *a*), Mary, Maria, Miriam

mariachis (mä´ rē-ä´ chĕs), wandering singers and musicians

mañana (män-yä´ n*a*), morning, tomorrow, later, in time to come

metate (mä-tä´ tĕ), curved stone for grinding corn or cocoa

Michoacán (mē´ chȯ-*a*-kän´)

monstruo (mōn-strōō´ ȯ), monster

muchas gracias (mōō´ chäs grä´ cē-*a*s), many thanks

olla (ō´ y*a*), pot, water jug

papá (pä-pä´), papa

Parícutin (pä-rē´ kōō-tēn´)

Pedro (pä´ drȯ), Peter

peso (pä´ sȯ), a silver coin of Mexico, then equal to about twenty cents in the United States

petate (pä-tä´ tĕ), sleeping mat

168

platillo (plä-tē´ yȯ), saucer

plato (plä´ tȯ), plate

Popocatepetl (pȯ-pō´ kä-tä´ pĕt-'l)

por (pōr), for, by

propina (prō-pē´ n*a*), a tip

¡**qué bonito**! (kä bō-nē´ tȯ), how beautiful!

rebozo (rä-bō´ sȯ), woman's shawl

señor (sēn-yōr´), Mr., sir

serape (sĕ-rä´ pĕ), shawl or wrap, often of gay colors

siesta (sĭ-ĕs´ t*a*), a midday or afternoon nap or rest

sombrero (sōm-brä´ rȯ), hat

tamale (tä-mä´ lĕ), a Mexican dish made of crushed corn and minced meat, seasoned with red peppers, etc., wrapped in corn husks and steamed

taza (tä´ z*a*), cup

turista (tōō-rēs´ t*a*), tourist

Uruapan (ōō-rwä´ pän)

veinte (vān´ tĕ), twenty

volcán (vōl-cän´), volcano